AS/A-LEVEL YEAR 1

STUDENT GUIDE

WJEC/Eduqas

Geography

Changing landscapes: Coastal landscapes

Tectonic hazards

Sue Warn

HODDER
EDUCATION
AN HACHETTE UK COMPANY

Hodder Education, an Hachette UK company, Blenheim Court, George Street, Banbury, Oxfordshire OX16 5BH

Orders

Bookpoint Ltd, 130 Park Drive, Milton Park, Abingdon, Oxfordshire OX14 4SE

tel: 01235 827827

fax: 01235 400401

e-mail: education@bookpoint.co.uk

Lines are open 9.00 a.m.–5.00 p.m., Monday to Saturday, with a 24-hour message answering service. You can also order through the Hodder Education website: www.hoddereducation.co.uk

ISBN 978-1-4718-6406-3

First printed 2017

Impression number 5 4 3 2

Year 2020 2019 2018 2017

This guide has been written specifically to support students preparing for the WJEC/Eduqas AS and A-level Geography examinations. The content has been neither approved nor endorsed by WJEC/Eduqas and remains the sole responsibility of the author.

Cover photo: dabldy/Fotolia; Figure 43 redrawn from NOAA/Center for Tsunami Research data.

Typeset by Integra Software Services Pvt Ltd, Pondicherry, India

Printed in Dubai

Hachette UK's policy is to use papers that are natural, renewable and recyclable products and made from wood grown in sustainable forests. The logging and manufacturing processes are expected to conform to the environmental regulations of the country of origin.

Contents

Content Guidance

Coastal landscapes

Tectonic hazards

Questions & Answers

■ Getting the most from this book

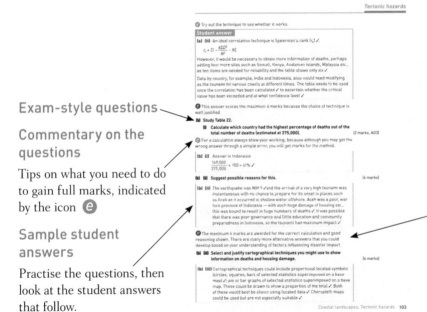

Exam-style questions

Commentary on the questions

Tips on what you need to do to gain full marks, indicated by the icon **e**

Sample student answers

Practise the questions, then look at the student answers that follow.

Commentary on sample student answers

Read the comments (preceded by the icon **e**) showing how many marks each answer would be awarded in the exam and exactly where marks are gained or lost.

■ About this book

Much of the knowledge and understanding needed for AS and A-level Geography builds on what you have learned for GCSE Geography but with an added focus on theories, geographical skills and techniques, and the specialised concepts listed in the specification. This guide has been designed to help you succeed in WJEC and Eduqas Geography AS and A-level exams.

This guide has two sections:

The **Content Guidance** summarises the key information that you need to know to be able to answer the examination questions with accuracy and depth. In particular, the meaning of key terms is made clear. You will also benefit from noting the exam tips, which provide further help in determining how to learn key aspects of the course. Knowledge check questions are designed to check your depth of knowledge.

The **Questions & Answers** section includes sample questions similar in style to those you might expect in the exam. There are sample student responses to these questions as well as detailed commentary giving further guidance in relation to what exam markers are looking for in order to award top marks. The best way to use this book is to read through the relevant topic area first before practising the questions. Only refer to the answers and comments after you have attempted the questions.

The topics covered in this guide are:

WJEC AS Unit 1 Changing landscapes
- Section A Changing landscapes: Coastal landscapes
- Section B Tectonic hazards

WJEC A2 Unit 4 Contemporary themes in geography
- Section A Tectonic hazards

Eduqas AS Component 1 Changing landscapes
- Section A Changing landscapes: Coastal landscapes
- Section B Tectonic hazards

Eduqas A-level Component 1: Changing landscapes and changing places
- Section A Changing landscapes: Coastal landscapes

Eduqas A-level Component 3: Contemporary themes in geography
- Section A Tectonic hazards

Content Guidance

Coastal landscapes

■ The operation of the coast as a system

The coastal zone is a dynamic open system. It has inputs and outputs of energy and materials such as sediment. Every stretch of coastline has stores of materials and energy, and a wide range of processes operate as flows to move these, such as river currents, waves, ocean currents and tides, and atmospheric processes such as wind. These all contribute to dynamic change.

When using systems theory it is often difficult to define the boundaries of the coastal systems (how far inland, how far out to sea). Figure 1 shows the widely accepted **spatial boundaries** of the coastal system. Within the coastal system there are a number of subsystems, such as cliff and beach systems.

Exam tip

Always use appropriate geographical terminology and use a geographical dictionary to define specialist terms.

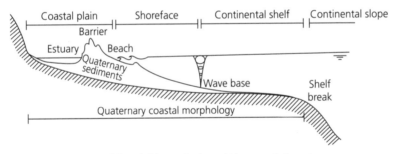

Figure 1 Spatial boundaries of the coastal system

The most useful approach to studying coastal systems includes the **process–response method**, which states that the morphology of any coastal landform is a product of the processes operating in the system (these processes are driven by energy and sediments). **Coastal cliff retreat** is a good example to explain this approach (see pp. 21–22).

The coastal sediment budget

Sediment and its movement is critical to the stability of a coastline. In order to manage a length of coastline it is important to know how much sediment is available, where it comes from, where it is stored, and how it leaves a particular coastal section. The identification of these factors is referred to as a **sediment budget** (Figure 2).

It is difficult to estimate sediment inputs and outputs, especially when considering sediment movements from and to offshore stores. The significance of each source (input) and output will vary according to different coastlines — for example in 'soft rock'

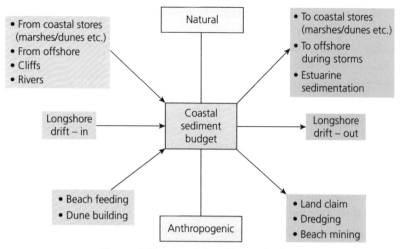

Figure 2 The coastal sediment budget

coastlines such as Barton on Sea, cliffs are the major terrestrial supplier of sediment (see p. 51), but in other parts of the world, such as Bangladesh, fluvial sediment is the dominant supply.

Outputs to the coastal system include longshore drift, loss to offshore, and transfer to sediment stores down the coast. Large volumes of sediment can be temporarily lost to the sediment budget in stores and, similarly, aeolian transfer can be a short-term loss. As Figure 2 shows, anthropogenic losses from beach mining, dredging etc. can also impact on total sediment losses from the system (see p. 47).

In a balanced budget, input and output volumes should be in equilibrium:

volume of sediment in = volume of sediment stored + volume of sediment out

Human actions, such as building dams or hard engineering coastal defences, can upset the sediment balance, as suddenly the inputs decline. If a replacement sediment source cannot be found, then the following situation will occur:

volume of sediment < volume of sediment stores + volume of sediment out

thus producing a net loss of sediment to the budget, and this accelerates erosion. Clearly, beach feeding or nourishment can represent a major input to help to balance the sediment budget.

Coastal sediment cells

In many countries, **sediment** or **littoral cells** have been identified as units of coastal management where the dominant processes influencing the sediment budget are generally uniform within a particular coastal stretch. For example, in Wales there are three main sediment and littoral cells, with boundaries formed from the promontories at St Davids Head, Bardsey Sound and Great Orme Head.

■ The movement of sand and shingle in the nearshore zone by littoral drift (longshore drift, see p. 25) has been found to occur in discrete, functionally separate cells. There are 11 major cells for England and Wales, with smaller subcells identified.

Knowledge check 1

Explain how beach nourishment can help to balance the sediment budget.

- A major cell is defined as a 'length of coastline and its associated nearshore area within which the movement of coarse sediments is largely self contained'.
- Sediment cells are functional systems as there is some movement across longshore drift divides. Littoral cells are therefore open systems.
- Sediment sinks (stores) occur where sediment transport paths meet.

The concept of equilibrium

Coasts are dynamic zones of rapid change. These changes occur frequently and are largely caused by changes in energy conditions. For example, during storms the morphology of the coast responds to changes in energy because it aims to exist in a state of equilibrium, i.e. when the amount of energy entering the coastal system is equal to the energy dissipated. There are three types of equilibrium:

1 **Steady state equilibrium:** where variations in energy and the morphological response do not deviate far from the long-term average. For example, where and when sea cliffs receive more or less equal atmospheric and marine energy (e.g. clouds and waves), the profile of the cliff tends to stay the same from year to year, especially for resistant rocks. In the same way, a beach receiving similar amounts of wave energy from one year to the next undergoes seasonal adjustments, but its **average** annual gradient stays the same.

2 **Meta-stable equilibrium:** where an environment switches between two or more states of equilibrium, stimulated by some sort of trigger. For example, the actions of high energy events, such as storms or a tsunami, can remove a whole beach in hours, or human actions such as the construction of a large breakwater or offshore dredging. This can rapidly switch a coastal system from one state of equilibrium to another, for example by removing or supplying large volumes of beach sediment.

3 **Dynamic equilibrium:** this also involves a change in equilibrium conditions but in a much more gradual manner than for meta-stable equilibrium, over a longer time period. A good example is the response of coasts to the gradual post-glacial eustatic rise in sea level, as large amounts of ice from ice sheets and ice caps have melted as a result of climate warming, so that wave energy actions occur higher up the shore, and cliff and beach profiles adjust as a consequence.

Equilibrium as a state does not apply to all coastal areas. Energy environments can change within just a few metres, spatially as well as temporally, which further complicates the issue.

System feedbacks

Understanding states of equilibrium requires some knowledge of feedbacks within the system. Feedbacks occur as the result of change in a system and they may be either positive or negative, switching the system to a new state of equilibrium or attempting to recover to the system's original state of equilibrium, respectively.

Knowledge check 2

Explain why littoral cells are classified as open systems.

Knowledge check 3

Explain how the coastal system is in a state of dynamic equilibrium.

Exam tip

There are certain key concepts that you must understand. These include systems, equilibrium and feedback.

Positive feedbacks therefore **amplify** the initial change in the system, so that, for example, the ridge of a coastal sand dune breached by storm wave erosion may be subsequently laterally undercut by wind erosion, so fragmenting the dune ridge and leaving it susceptible to further wave erosion. Ultimately the whole dune ridge may be driven further inland and a new state of equilibrium reached.

Negative feedbacks diminish or dampen the effect of change. For example, sand eroded during a storm from the front of the embryo and fore dunes at the back of the beach, may be redeposited offshore as sand bars, which help to protect the beach dune system from erosion by slowing waves and dissipating the wave energy reaching the dune front.

Human intervention often leads to apparently unforeseen and undesirable feedbacks, often as a result of inappropriate coastal management.

Summary

- The coastal system includes inputs, outputs, stores and transfers of energy and materials.
- The sediment budget refers to the amount of sediment available, where it comes from, where it is stored, and how it leaves a particular coastal section.
- Sediment cells are units of coastal management where the dominant processes influencing the sediment budget are uniform within a stretch of coast.
- Coasts are dynamic zones of rapid and frequent changes, largely caused by changes in energy conditions, for example during storms.
- Dynamic equilibrium involves a gradual change, over a long time period, for example in response to post-glacial eustatic rise in sea level as climate warming causes ice melting, so that wave actions occur higher up the shore, and shore profiles adjust.

Temporal variations and their influence on coastal environments

Tides, waves and currents are key inputs of energy into the coastal system as they have the potential to erode, transport and deposit material. All three are rapid processes, in that they operate from the instantaneous through to annual timescales but rarely on decadal scales, except in terms of cumulative change.

Tides result from the gravitational attraction on water of the moon and the sun, with the moon having twice the impact of the sun. All coasts are influenced to some extent by tides, but only a few types of coastline, such as **lowland sandy estuarine coasts**, can be said to be tide-dominated.

Tidal frequency

Most coastlines, such as all open Atlantic coastlines, experience **semi-diurnal** tides, i.e. two high and two low tides approximately every 24 hours. However, some places, such as Antarctica, receive genuinely **diurnal** tides — one high tide and one low tide each day, as a result of local factors.

As the respective motions of the Earth, moon and sun go through **regular cycles**, the gravitational forces change and, therefore, so do the tides.

Twice a month the sun and moon are aligned so that their gravitational forces are combined and therefore there is a strong gravitational pull — this leads to above-average tides called **spring tides** which, if combined with strong winds and storms, can cause significant landform changes high up on the shore. Twice a month the sun and moon are at right angles with respect to the Earth. As their gravitational forces act in different (opposed) directions they are lessened, so lower than average tides result, called **neap tides**. On a biannual basis the largest of the spring tides occur at the vernal (spring) and autumnal equinoxes, when the sun is 'overhead' at the Equator.

If you look at tide tables you will see that high and low water times in most parts of the UK are separated by more than six hours, so that high and low tides occur slightly later each day.

The overall effect of tides is seen in smaller systems because of variations in ocean depth, uneven sea bed topography with deep basins separated by shallower continental shelves and continents, and the shape of these landmasses. Because of the Earth's rotation (Coriolis force) tides circulate around **amphidromic points**.

High and low tides therefore occur at different times along coasts such as in the UK, as water swirls around the amphidromic points.

> **Exam tip**
>
> At first, tides seem complicated to understand. It becomes much easier to understand the variations when you look at tide tables.

Tidal range

The height difference between high water and low water during the monthly tidal cycle is known as the **tidal range**. Annually, this is highest at spring tides and lowest at neap tides.

Tidal range is important for coastal geomorphology because it influences a number of physical processes.

- Tidal range determines the vertical distances over which coastal processes operate, especially wave activity. On a micro-tidal coast (tidal range of less than 2 m, e.g. eastern Australia), wave breaking is concentrated in a narrow vertical zone throughout the tidal cycle, so well-defined erosional features such as wave-cut notches are formed at the foot of cliffs. On a macro-tidal coast (tidal range in excess of 6 m, e.g. most of the UK coast, and parts of North America such as the Bay of Fundy, which has the greatest tidal range in the world), wave energy is distributed over a wide area, so its erosional capacity is relatively less, resulting in more depositional features.
- During the diurnal rise and fall of tides, wetting and drying of the substrata occurs. In a macro-tidal environment, more substrata is exposed or submerged and therefore affected by processes such as salt weathering. Sand dunes are more likely to develop in a macro-tidal environment, as here there is a wide expanse of deposited beach sand which dries and can be subsequently transported landward by aeolian processes.

Currents

Currents are clearly identifiable water flows operating in the coastal zone. **Tidal currents** are associated with tidal movements. Other currents include **shore normal currents** to and from shore zones, onshore and offshore currents, longshore currents which are responsible for longshore drift, rip currents and river currents.

As water rises with the tides it produces tidal currents. It floods the intertidal zone (**flood tide**) causing entrainment and deposition of material. The falling tide is the **ebb tide**, which carries material in the reverse direction. These tidal currents have maximum velocity at their midpoints, while at high and low water, current velocity slackens considerably, leading to sediment deposition. As with rivers (Hjulström curve), there are critical current velocity **thresholds** for tidal currents to transport different particle sizes. Therefore muds are usually found in low energy low and high intertidal areas, while sand shoals occur in mid intertidal areas. Overall there is considerable transfer of sediment from offshore to nearshore and back again within the intertidal zone on a daily basis during every ebb–flood tidal cycle.

Where waves approach the shore with their crests parallel to the coastline, shore normal currents occur. Water is carried up the beach but there has to be a return flow — rip currents occur in fairly evenly spaced locations along the beach — and they flow back at speeds up to $1\,\text{m s}^{-1}$ through the advancing waves. Note the contrasts with oblique waves (see p. 25). River currents are also powerful currents, which transport both river sediment and fresh water into the coastal zone. Energetic flows are periodic and associated with high levels of river flood discharge.

see p. 25

Knowledge check 4

Explain the term 'threshold' in the context of sediment entrainment and deposition at the coast.

Constructive and destructive waves

The classification of waves is based on their geomorphological action and the way in which they break upon the shore.

Landforms are the result of inputs of energy to surface and near surface materials. At the coast, the main source of energy is waves generated by the wind. The frictional effect of the wind on the seawater surface produces motion in the upper surface of the water (Figure 3). This motion is only a wave shape on the water surface and not an actual forward movement of water. Individual water particles move in a circular path as the wave shape moves across the water surface, as sea waves are caused directly

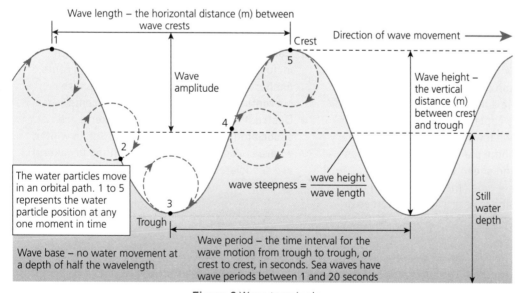

Figure 3 Wave terminology

by wind. The stronger and more persistent the wind, the higher the amplitude of the waves and the more energy there is available for 'work'.

As a wave reaches shallower water at the coast, the circular water motion in the wave shape is affected by the sea floor. As water depth decreases (Figure 4) the water path movements change from a circular to an elliptical shape: wave length and velocity decrease and wave height increases. The wave steepens and then breaks on the shore to produce different types of breaking wave, depending on the ocean floor gradient.

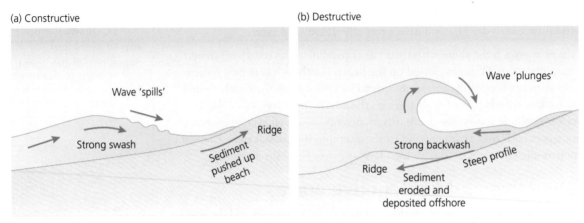

Figure 4 Constructive and destructive waves

This variation in wave type, often on an **annual** basis, has an impact on sediment mobility and coastal morphology — the extent of wave energy dissipation determines whether coasts become erosional, depositional, or stable.

Summary

- Tides, waves and currents input energy into the coastal system as they erode, transport and deposit material.
- All coasts are influenced by tides, which result from the gravitational attraction on water of the moon and the sun, with the moon having twice the impact of the sun.
- Most coastlines experience semi-diurnal tides (two high and two low tides approximately every 24 hours), but some places have diurnal tides (one high tide and one low tide each day).
- Spring tides occur when the sun and moon are aligned, combining their gravitational forces to create a strong pull. Neap tides occur when the sun and moon are at right angles to the Earth and their gravitational forces act in opposite directions.
- Currents are identifiable water flows which include tidal currents, shore normal currents, onshore and offshore currents, longshore currents, rip currents and river currents.
- Destructive waves (plunging breakers) are associated with stronger winds, often in winter, whereas constructive waves (spilling breakers) are associated with less powerful winds in summer.

▪ Landforms and landscape systems, their distinctive features and distribution

High energy rocky coastal environments

The morphology and behaviour of rocky coastlines reflects the interplay between geological factors (rock structure and lithology (rock type)) and weathering and erosional processes.

Rocky coasts are **erosive** coasts, and are continually being cut back. While there is a comparatively slow rate of change averaged over long periods, recent research has shown that rocky coasts can be dynamic over short timescales such as during winter storms, so they are called high energy coasts.

Rocky coast erosion is accomplished by a wide range of processes working together. These processes can be grouped into three main types: mass movement, rock breakdown processes and marine 'rock removal' processes.

- **Mass movements** such as rock falls or landslides, depending on the rock type, are common because of the prevailing steep and therefore unstable slopes. All types of mass movement are **episodic**, occurring more commonly in winter as a result of more powerful waves undercutting the cliff base.
- **Rock breakdown processes** are physical, chemical and biological processes (types of **weathering**) that weaken and loosen rock material, making it available for removal by marine processes.
- **Rock removal processes** depend on the action of waves — energetic wave conditions in a concentrated micro-tidal environment are particularly effective, both in causing abrasion and hydraulic action. The larger and more powerful the waves, the greater the efficiency of the cross-shore and longshore sediment transport processes by tidal currents to remove loose material and keep rocky coasts 'fresh' from debris.

Classic examples for the study of rocky coastlines can be found in Dyfed (Pembrokeshire) or southern Gower in Wales, as well as in many places around the world such as the Great Coast Road in southern Victoria, Australia. They are frequently classified as wave-dominated coastlines.

> **Knowledge check 5**
>
> Explain what is meant by 'episodic events' such as landslides.

Low energy sandy coastal environments

Low energy coastal environments tend to produce largely depositional coasts with sandy beaches often backed by sand dunes, with accompanying depositional features such as spits, bars and tidal mudflats. Low energy environments can be macro- or micro-tidal but have shallow shoreline gradients with constructive waves (spilling breakers) pushing sediment shorewards.

While low energy conditions are prevalent, they are frequently interspersed by dramatic storm events which upset the dynamic equilibrium and lead to major changes in beach and bar morphology. On a stretch of lowland coast you will find both wave-dominated coastal stretches of beaches, barriers and dunes, and tide-dominated stretches of coast usually around estuaries.

Examples of low energy coastal environments are widespread, often interspersed with rocky shorelines. Extensive stretches of lowland low energy coastlines occur along the German Baltic coast, the Netherlands coast, much of southern and eastern USA and the Lagos coast of Nigeria.

Summary

- High energy rocky coastlines are erosive, continually being cut back by mass movement, rock breakdown and rock removal processes, and their morphology reflects the combination of geological factors (rock structure and type) and weathering and erosional processes.
- Low energy coasts are largely depositional, with shallow shoreline gradients and constructive waves pushing sediment shorewards, building sandy and shingle beaches that are often backed by sand dunes, and storm beaches.
- Erosional landforms include cliffs, shore platforms and wave-cut notches.
- Depositional landforms include sandy and shingle beaches, sand dunes, spits, bars and lagoons, tombolos and cuspate forelands.

Factors affecting coastal processes and landforms

Waves

The essential features of a wave were defined on p. 11 (see Figure 3). Most of the waves affecting coastal zones are entirely wind generated (except tsunamis and storm surges), caused by the frictional drag between wind and the water surface. The amount of energy transferred between the wind and the water depends on:

- wind velocity
- wind duration
- fetch (the distance over open water the wind blows to generate the waves)
- orientation of the coast to the waves

The greatest energy transfer occurs when strong winds blow in the same direction over a long distance for a long period of time, for example the great swell waves driven across the Atlantic by the prevailing southwesterly winds. Certain coasts receive high energy waves — this includes all of the west coast of the UK — as they are orientated towards these waves.

Waves bring huge amounts of energy into the coastal system and, as they approach the land, they are modified as a result of the decreasing water depth. Different types of waves are described in Table 1.

> **Knowledge check 6**
>
> Define the following aspects of wave terminology: wavelength, amplitude, frequency.

Table 1 Types of waves

Wave type	Description
Spilling Low energy	Steep: low-angled shore gradient, break at some distance from the shore, foam forms at wave crest and becomes a line of surf as waves approach shore. Strong swash. Constructs beach. Low frequency
Plunging High energy	Steep: steep-angled shore gradient, steep fronted, tend to curl over and plunge down onto the shore. Strong **backwash** (felt as undertow). Destroys beach
Surging	Gentle: steep-angled shore gradient, tend not to break completely, top of wave breaks close to shore, water slides up and down shore

Wave refraction

As waves approach a coastline, the direction of wave approach is modified by the bottom topography of the sea bed. Wave refraction causes the wave energy from the breaking waves to vary along the coastline (Figure 5). This wave energy becomes concentrated at headlands and disperses around bays. The complex interaction of coastal configuration, offshore topography, exposure, wave fetch and landforms helps to explain variations in processes and landforms. Waves are refracted around a spit to give it a curved end or hook (see Figure 12, p. 27). You can sketch wave refraction patterns for any chosen stretch of coastline using Google Earth Images.

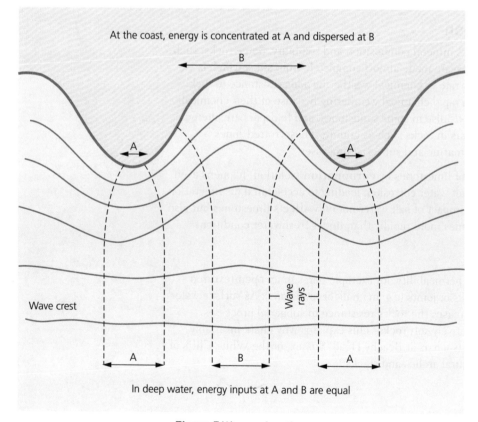

Figure 5 Wave refraction

Wave reflection

Along rocky coastlines (p. 21) where there is deep water offshore, the waves are reflected back from the cliffs (known as the **clapotis** effect) and do not break at the shoreline. Wave reflection can also take place on very steep beaches or against sea walls. The interaction of reflected and incoming waves creates a **standing wave**.

The lithology of the coastline

A number of factors combine to make lithology (the make-up of the rock) an important influence on coastal processes and landforms.

Hardness

As a result of heating and compression during their formation, igneous and metamorphic rocks are harder and therefore more resistant to erosion. These types of rock form many high cliffs in northwest Britain. In contrast, many of the rocks that form the coastlines of southern and eastern Britain are 'soft rocks' — unconsolidated sand and clays of Tertiary age, as well as deposits of glacial boulder clay and gravels. Other factors being equal, these 'soft' rocks tend to be easily eroded, especially if the cliff bases are poorly protected by beaches (average recession rate of 3–6 m per year; after a storm, 10–25 m is not uncommon). An extreme example of erosion rates of 30 m per year has been recorded in the ash from the Krakatoa eruption in coastal Sumatra.

Chemical composition

Chemical composition includes mineral composition and solubility. Some rocks, such as quartzite or most sandstones, are made almost completely from silica which is chemically inert. The very low rate of chemical weathering adds resistance to rock. Other rocks are more prone to rapid chemical weathering because of their chemical composition. Iron compounds oxidise in some sandstones, and feldspars are altered into clay minerals by **hydrolysis** in rocks such as granite. These 'rotted zones' increase vulnerability to both marine and subaerial processes.

The chemical decomposition of limestones by **carbonation** (solution) happens even more rapidly. It is caused by salt water corrosion, leading to accelerated disintegration of some shore platforms. The impact of salt water not only affects limestones but also causes basalt to weather 14 times more rapidly than under freshwater conditions.

Permeability

A further lithological factor is permeability, for example pores in an open-textured limestone or fissures and cracks or joints (e.g. in chalk or limestone). As surface water seeps through the cliffs, it increases the rock's resistance to subaerial processes, thereby adding strength to relatively soft rocks. This explains why chalk invariably forms high near-vertical cliffs (such as at Beachy Head, Sussex, or the White Cliffs of Dover, Kent) and supports natural arches and stacks.

Knowledge check 7

Explain how clapotis affects cliff recession rates.

The structure of the coastline

'Structure' can be defined as the way rocks are disposed or geologically arranged. Folding and faulting therefore provide a range of rock types with lithologies of different resistance to subaerial and marine processes — i.e. the way less resistant rocks are more easily exploited.

Joints, faults and folds

The amount of joints, bedding planes and faults in a rock has a significant impact on the rates of weathering (both freeze–thaw and chemical). Where joints and bedding planes occur at high densities this weakens the rock and makes it subject to increased subaerial and marine erosion.

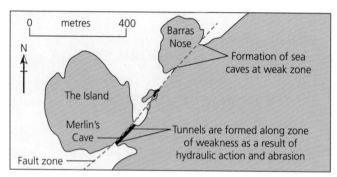

Figure 6 The impact of the fault at Tintagel

Faults or isolated master joints can be exploited by the sea to form a range of micro-features, as at Tintagel in North Cornwall (see Figure 6). Narrow inlets (geos), such as those on the Island of Skomer, Pembrokeshire, develop along faults, which are a zone of weakness (a shatter zone). Folds (anticlines and synclines), where the rocks are stretched or compressed, also form weaker areas, for example at Saundersfoot near Tenby.

In conclusion, the combined impacts of structure and lithology play a major role in determining both major and minor landforms, especially where coasts are composed of 'hard rocks'.

Exam tip

A case study of the Pembrokeshire coast is available at www.curriculum-press.co.uk

Summary

- Coastal processes and landforms are affected by wave characteristics, and the lithology and structural geology of the coast.
- Wave characteristics, including fetch, wave type, wave energy, orientation, refraction and reflection, all affect coastal processes. Spilling low energy waves construct the beach, whereas plunging waves with a strong backwash destroy the beach. Wave refraction causes wave energy to be concentrated at headlands and dispersed around bays.
- The lithology of the rock — its hardness, chemical composition and solubility — influences differential erosion, transportation, deposition and coastal landforms.
- The rock structure — the effects of folding and faulting, the amount of joints, bedding planes and faults, and their arrangement — influence the shape and distribution of landforms.

■ Processes of coastal weathering, mass movement, erosion and the associated landforms

Subaerial weathering

Although the same range of weathering processes occurs at the coast as inland, the presence of corrosive seawater and the daily effect of tides wetting and drying rock bring additional destructive influences. The key influences on the type and rate of weathering are geology and climate.

Physical/mechanical weathering breaks off rock fragments of varying sizes which fall to the foot of the cliff where they can protect the cliff from erosion (see Table 2).

Table 2 Effects of physical/mechanical weathering processes on coasts

Weathering process	Effect
Salt water crystal growth	Crystals (e.g. salt) grow when seawater that collects in cracks in the cliff face evaporates. As they grow, crystals exert pressure on the rock (most important)
Freeze–thaw	Repeated freezing and thawing of water causes a type of crystal growth that is most effective on high latitude coasts with significant precipitation
Wetting and drying (water-layer weathering)	Expansion and contraction of minerals is most effective on clay and in macro-tidal environments

Chemical weathering acts to decompose rock (certain types of rock are more susceptible) by altering the minerals in the rock (see Table 3).

Table 3 Effects of chemical weathering processes on coasts

Weathering process	Effect
Solution	Solubility of minerals depends on temperature and acidity of the water. Limestones are affected by carbonation, although they may be less soluble in seawater. Spray charged with carbonic acid leads to honeycomb weathering
Hydration	Minerals absorb water, weakening their crystal structure. Rock is then more susceptible to other weathering processes
Hydrolysis	Reaction between mineral and water related to hydrogen ion concentration in water, particularly affects feldspar minerals in granite
Oxidation/reduction	Adding or removing oxygen. Oxidation results from oxygen dissolved in water and particularly affects rocks with a high iron content. Reduction is common under waterlogged conditions
Chelation	Organic acids, produced by plant roots and decaying organic matter, bind to metal ions, causing weathering

Biotic weathering by plant roots is particularly active on vegetated upper slopes of cliffs, and opens up the cliff face to other destructive processes. Burrowing animals cause weathering of soft rocks such as clay and can also disturb coastal sand dunes.

Mass movement

The type of mass movement that occurs is closely related to the geological structure and lithology of the coastline, the weathering processes which loosen the material on the cliff face, as well as the controls imposed by climate, past and present. Vegetation can also have a retarding impact.

Mass movement can be defined as 'the downslope movement of material under the influence of gravity'. Many instances of mass movement, which can occur very suddenly (within minutes), are triggered by undercutting by wave action at the base of a coastal cliff.

There are four types of *rapid* mass movement.

1 **Rock fall**. Blocks of rock, dislodged by weathering, fall to the cliff foot. For example, in Svalbard (a high latitude periglacial region) rock blocks are loosened by freeze–thaw action.

2 **Rock slides**. Blocks of rock slide down the cliff face, especially where rocks are dipping steeply towards the sea. This is common on the carboniferous limestone cliffs of Tenby and Gower in South Wales.

3 **Rock toppling**. Blocks or even columns of rock, weakened by weathering, fall seawards. This has occurred in the columnar basalt of the Giants Causeway in County Antrim, in Northern Ireland.

4 **Rotational slides and slumps**. In a rotational slide, sections of the cliff give way along a well-defined concave slip surface. The fallen material stays as an identifiable mass off the shore because it is often composed of cohesive clays or boulder clay, so it may take a month for it to be eroded by the sea.

Slumps occur where permeable rock overlays impermeable rock, such as at Christchurch and Barton on Sea (southern England). They are also common in unconsolidated rock (e.g. the sandy boulder clay deposits of North Norfolk and Holderness, both in eastern England). The subaerial processes are particularly active after periods of heavy rainfall, which lead to saturation and subsequent lubrication. A critical threshold is reached, triggering mass movement and slope failure, and mudflows.

Slow mass movements include:
- **Creep:** the extremely slow (imperceptible) downslope movement of regolith (the loose material including soil above the bedrock).
- **Solifluction:** the slow downslope movement of regolith, saturated by the melting of the active layer above the permafrost (in the summer of periglacial climate regions). There is some evidence that many parts of the UK experienced this type of movement in the last Ice Age.

Exam tip

Be clear about the differences between weathering and erosion, and between subaerial and marine erosion.

Knowledge check 8

Explain the difference between rotational slides and slumps.

Marine erosion

A number of wave erosional processes exist, which work in combination.

- **Hydraulic action** results from waves breaking on bedded, jointed or faulted rocks that can create hydraulic pressure in these structural voids, which may lead to weakening and readying of the rocks for further wave action.
- **Quarrying** occurs where powerful waves remove loose blocks.
- **Attrition** occurs when detached rocks break down through rubbing and banging against each other, gradually rounding the blocks as well as reducing their size.
- **Corrasion** occurs when waves use the material provided by attrition and abrasion as tools to further erode the rock.
- **Corrosion** occurs when rocks such as limestones are chemically attacked by waves.

Characteristics and formation of coastal erosional landforms

Cliffs and shore platforms

A cliff may be defined as 'any coastal slope affected by marine processes', although subaerial processes also play a significant role in cliff formation.

The cliff profile is determined by a number of factors. A variation in the balance of the inputs can result in different cliff morphologies in different locations (Figure 7). Cliff morphology may be determined by the following.

- **Geology**. The hardness and structure of the rock are very important in the formation of cliffs, with igneous and metamorphic rocks, and some sedimentary rocks such as limestone and sandstone, invariably forming steep cliffs. In contrast, unconsolidated rocks such as clays and sands usually result in low-angled cliffs. However, **constant** marine erosion at the cliff base can lead to frequent slope failure and, if the debris is removed, can again leave a steep slope ready to be undercut once more.
  Steep cliffs are also associated with either horizontal or vertical geological structure. The angle of inclination of the bedding planes (dip) is important, with seaward-dipping cliffs having low angles and landward-dipping cliffs having near-vertical faces.
- **The balance between marine erosion (wave activity) and subaerial processes**. Sufficiently energetic waves, usually highest along mid-latitude coasts, are required not only to erode the cliff but also to remove the debris created by wave erosion, as piles of subaerial debris tend to protect the cliff.
- **Inherited characteristics**. The sea may rework steep slopes initially formed by non-marine processes under different sea level situations. For example, some plunging cliffs that rise abruptly from deepwater fjords, were originally sides of submerged glaciated valleys.

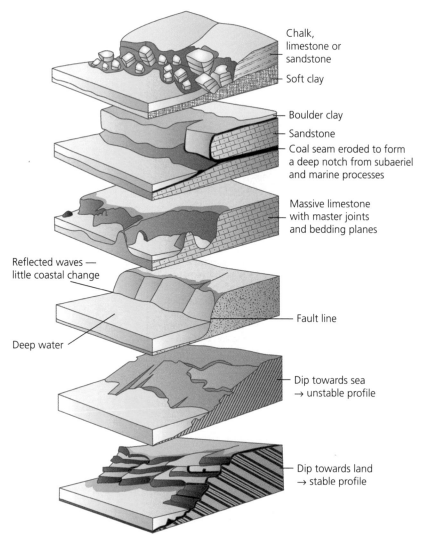

Chalk, limestone or sandstone

Soft clay

Boulder clay

Sandstone

Coal seam eroded to form a deep notch from subaeriel and marine processes

Massive limestone with master joints and bedding planes

Reflected waves — little coastal change

Fault line

Deep water

Dip towards sea → unstable profile

Dip towards land → stable profile

Figure 7 Cliff profiles found in the UK

Cliff retreat and the formation of shore platforms

The sequence of cliff retreat (Figure 8) often proceeds as follows:

- A **wave-cut notch** is formed by wave quarrying and corrosion at the base of the cliff, which effectively undermines the cliff, causing slope failure either via slumping (soft rocks) or vertical cliff collapse.
- Where cliffs are fronted by a narrow shore, a cycle of notch formation, cliff failure, debris removal and cliff retreat takes place.
- In time, a wide shore platform develops. The cliffs are then no longer within reach of any marine action other than storm waves at the highest spring tides, so in time the cliff profile becomes degraded.

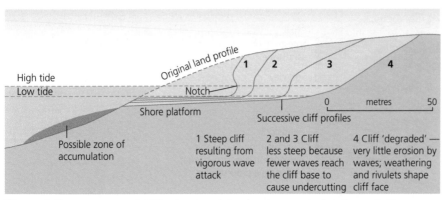

Figure 8 The sequence of cliff retreat and the development of a shore platform

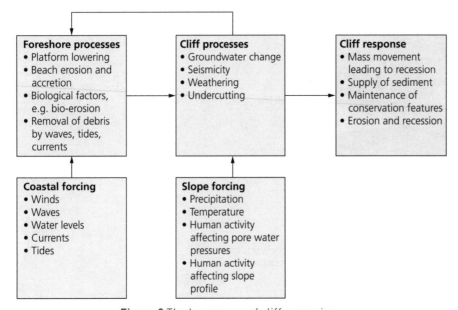

Figure 9 The key causes of cliff recession

The combined impact of the causes of cliff recession (see Figure 9) on cliff geology plays a key role in the rates of cliff retreat, which vary considerably as shown in Table 4.

Table 4 Average rates of cliff retreat per year by rock type

Granites	Limestones	Chalk	Shales	Clays	Unconsolidated glacial deposits
Resistant	1 cm	10 cm	1 m	10 m	100 m

Note: this is a log scale

Shore platforms

Intertidal shore platforms (sometimes known as wave-cut platforms) are created by wave quarrying and abrasion, but bio-erosion and salt weathering during tidal exposure are also significant — hence the abandonment of the term 'wave-cut platform'. Shore platforms are relatively flat expanses of gently sloping (usually 1–5° seaward) rock, found at the foot of a cliff and extending out to sea. Shore platforms also show the influence of rock structure (where the rocks are steeply dipping and resistant, the platforms are narrow and ridged) and lithology (differential erosion leads to variations of micro-relief), for example the ridges caused by resistant igneous dykes on the shore platforms of Arran in Scotland. Platform width is ultimately finite, as increasingly wide platforms dissipate wave energy before it reaches the cliff base.

Headland and **bay formation** results from the differential erosion of juxtaposed rocks of varying resistance, especially where the coast is **discordant**, with the structural trend at approximately right angles to the coastal trend. This is in contrast to **concordant coasts**, where **cove** formation is the key feature, such as in the 'classic' stretch of coastline on the World Heritage Coast of Dorset.

The formation of micro-features

There are *two* likely sequences of development. Initially, **sea caves** develop (Figure 10), their distribution controlled by geological weaknesses such as master joints, major bedding planes, faults etc.

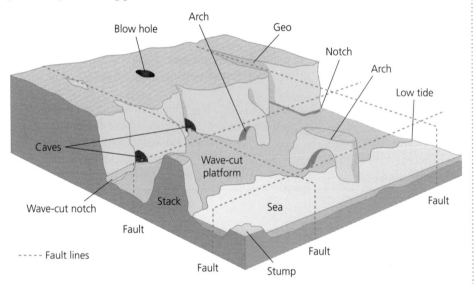

Figure 10 Cliff architecture

Sequence 1: The impact of air and water forced up into the caves by wave action can lead to the development of vertical shafts and tunnels upwards to the ground surface to form a **blow hole**, e.g. Spouting Horn in Kauai, Hawaii.

Air and water are forced through the blow hole by breaking waves, at certain tides and particular wind directions, with an explosive force. This causes large pressure changes in the cave and further erosion.

The blow hole roof may collapse to form a **geo** or inlet. Alternatively, differential erosion may exploit the weakness of the fault or shatter zone to form a very long narrow gully, or geo, for example in Orkney.

Sequence 2: Differential erosion may result in adjacent caves, perhaps on either side of a headland, meeting to form a **natural arch**, which may last perhaps 50–100 years before it collapses.

Knowledge check 9

Explain why the term 'wave-cut platform' is an inaccurate one and has been superseded by 'shore platform'.

Exam tip

Differential erosion is a key concept. Use the case study of headland and bay formation along the World Heritage Coast of Dorset to identify name examples.

The collapsed arch can lead to development of a sea stack (but not all sea stacks are initially arches), e.g. the Old Man of Hoy in Orkney. Frequently, stacks are eroded away to form **stumps**. Some stacks, such as Charley's Garden at Seaton Sluice on the Northumberland coast, have now vanished.

Summary

- Subaerial processes include physical, chemical and biotic weathering, and mass movement such as landslides, slumps and rock falls.
- Weathering breaks off rock fragments of varying sizes which fall to the foot of the cliff, protecting the cliff from erosion. Physical weathering includes salt water crystal growth, freeze–thaw, and wetting and drying. Chemical weathering decomposes the rock by solution, hydration, hydrolysis, oxidation/reduction and chelation. Biotic weathering includes the work of plant roots and burrowing animals.
- Mass movement is the downslope movement of material aided by gravity. Rapid mass movement processes include rock fall, rock slides, rock toppling and rotational slides and slumps. Slow mass movements include creep and solifluction.
- Marine erosional processes include hydraulic action, abrasion (corrasion), corrosion and attrition. Erosion by waves depends on wave characteristics and the wave environment of the coastline, the geological environment and the morphology of the coastline.
- Coastal landforms include cliffs, headlands and bays, shore platforms and micro-features such as the cave–arch–stack–stump sequence, geos and blow holes.
- Cliff morphology is influenced by geology, especially the hardness and structure of the rock, the balance between marine erosion and subaerial processes, and inherited characteristics such as submerged glaciated valleys.
- Headland and bay formation results from the differential erosion of juxtaposed rocks of varying resistance, especially where the coast is discordant. In contrast, on concordant coasts, cove formation is the key feature.

∎ Processes of coastal transport and deposition and the associated landforms

Modes of sediment transport

Once in motion the mode of transport that a sediment grain is subject to is largely determined by the mass (size) of the grain and the speed of the currents.

- **Bedload** is where grains are 'supported' by either continuous **traction** or intermittent contact (**saltation**) with the sea floor. When traction occurs, the grains slide along the sea bed. Traction is a relatively slow mode of transport — while strong currents can transport pebbles, cobbles and boulders, weak currents will only transport sand-sized particles. Only the strongest currents can move pebbles by **saltation**, where grains are bounced along the sea bed. Saltation is an important mechanism for sand transport by the wind (aeolian).
- **Suspended load** is where grains are supported by turbulence, typically when moderate currents are transporting silt or clays in **suspension**.
- **Solution** involves corroded particles from limestones being dissolved by salt water and carried by the sea.

Knowledge check 10

Explain why beach deposits are generally 'sorted'.

Overall, sand particles are the easiest to transport at relatively low speeds, whereas cohesive fine clay particles and larger gravels, pebbles and cobbles, require higher speed currents. Different transport speeds mean that sediment is better sorted over time, through the progressive differential transport of grains of different sizes.

Longshore drift

Just as constructive waves 'swash' materials onto the beach, waves that are influenced by **prevailing winds** move material *along* the shoreline.

Longshore drift most commonly takes place when the prevailing winds blow at an oblique angle to the shoreline and therefore cause incoming waves to approach the shore at an oblique angle and the swash pushes pebbles and sand up onto the beach diagonally (see Figure 11).

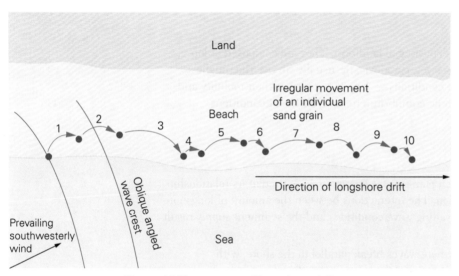

Figure 11 The process of longshore drift

However, under the influence of gravity, the backwash from the same wave moves back towards the sea at right angles, carrying some of the deposited beach material with it. The long-term impact of these alternate swash and backwash movements is to move sand, pebbles and gravel along the shore from one end of the beach to the other.

Longshore drift is an irregular process on a day-to-day basis — its direction depends on both the direction of prevailing winds and the orientation of the shoreline. Longer term, over months and years, longshore drift operates in a preferred direction — for example on the UK's south-facing coasts it transports materials eastwards and on west-facing coasts this direction is northward.

Overall, longshore drift is especially marked on straight coastlines but, providing the downdrift output of sediment is matched by updrift input, the beach system remains in **equilibrium**. Only if the supply of material is disrupted is there a need to replenish and maintain beach stores (by beach feeding and groyne construction).

Deposition

Deposition of material in open water occurs when the energy of the transporting water becomes too low to transport the sediment, with the sediment deposited being directly proportional to the mass (size) of the sediment (Stokes law). Where clay particles aggregate together to form **flocs**, **flocculation** increases the fall velocity and therefore speeds up deposition. In shallow waters and beach situations the energy of the waves causes differential deposition, with the largest cobbles and boulders thrown above the high water mark by storm waves to form a **storm beach** (as at Newgale, Pembrokeshire) — one example of sediment sorting.

Characteristics and formation of coastal depositional landforms

Beaches

Beaches are the most common depositional landform. They are composed of loose, unconsolidated sands and pebbles yet, paradoxically, usually survive the roughest storms and most energetic wave conditions — largely because of their mobility and their ability to adjust their dynamic equilibrium to many different conditions.

Beach forms

Large-scale landforms

The main influence on the beach plan is wave energy — in particular its relationship with the prevailing wave direction. The interactions between the amount of longshore movement of sediment, the prevailing wave conditions and the sediment supply result in three main types of beaches.

1 **Swash-aligned beaches**, where waves break parallel to the shore, with little longshore drift. Sediment movement is onshore–offshore.
2 **Drift-aligned beaches**, where waves arrive at an oblique angle and considerable longshore drift occurs. Plenty of sediment available.
3 **Zeta-formed beaches**, at an oblique angle to dominant wave approach with longshore drift, but where headlands at each end cause wave refraction and block sediment movement. At the far end (away from the dominant wave direction) sediment builds up in front of a headland.

Spits

Spits are linear deposits of sand and shingle, attached to land at the **proximal** end but free at the **distal** end. They are found where:
- the coast has an abrupt change of direction, such as at an estuary or bay, both of which are low energy environments
- there is a ready supply of sediment, particularly sand and shingle
- longshore drift is active
- tidal range is micro-tidal (less than 2 m) so wave energy is focused into a restricted zone

Many spits have recurved or hooked distal ends, which may result from wave refraction, currents or a combination of the two. Spits create sheltered areas behind them in which salt marshes frequently form (see Figure 12).

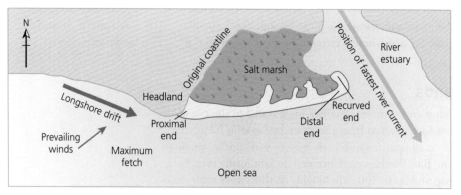

Figure 12 The main features of a spit

Longshore drift moves the sand and shingle along the shore and, where there is a major change in the coastline trend, the longshore drift may continue to deposit sediments into the sea, gradually building up the spit. Most spits grow at fairly rapid rates. Orford Ness in Suffolk, for example, is extending southwards at a rate of up to 15 m per year and has diverted the River Alde 12 km south.

Spits can develop so that they form a bar, cutting off large areas of sea and creating coastal lagoons. The 98 km long Neringa Spit in the Baltic Sea has virtually sealed off the lagoon behind it, so the Lithuanian port authorities have to dredge a channel through it to keep the port of Klaipeda open. A pair of spits facing each other on either side of a coastal indentation can sometimes occur, as at Christchurch Harbour.

A spit is often in a state of precarious equilibrium between inputs of wind, wave energy, tidal energy and sediment and is therefore subject to frequent change.

Cuspate forelands

Cuspate forelands are triangular-shaped projections with an apex pointing out to sea. They vary considerably in scale: while the Dungeness foreland extends for around 30 km along the Kent coast, projecting about 15 km into the English Channel, some of the cuspate forelands in North Carolina on the east coast of the USA, such as Cape Hatteras, extend up to 150 km along the side attached to the mainland.

Cuspate forelands seem to be present where sediment, moved by longshore drift, becomes trapped when an equilibrium is reached between sediment inputs and energy available to move it.

The Dungeness cuspate foreland (the most extensive foreland in Europe) developed from two opposing directions of swell and the consequent longshore drift.

Tombolos

Tombolos are complex features that develop when longshore drift joins an island onto either the mainland or to a larger island. A spectacular tombolo — the Tombolo di Orbetello in Tuscany — was formed where two sand spits have joined the former Monte Argentano Island onto the mainland, forming a large lagoon. Some smaller tombolos on the Isles of Scilly have formed where a cuspate foreland has linked up with islands.

Bars and barrier islands

Bars are elongated deposits of sand and shingle, usually lying parallel to the coastline, laid down by constructive waves and separated from the shore by lagoons. They may vary in scale from comparatively small features just a few metres wide and a couple of hundred metres long, such as Loe Bar, Porthleven, Cornwall, to landforms over 1 km wide, hundreds of kilometres long and up to 100 m in height. At this larger scale, bars are known as barrier beaches or **barrier islands** and, unlike some of the smaller bars, they are not submerged at high tide.

In Europe the biggest system of barrier islands is the Friesian Islands, which stretch from the northern part of the Netherlands into North Germany, enclosing a huge shallow sea, the Wadden Sea.

Bars and barrier islands typically occur in seas with shallow offshore gradients and a low tidal range (less than 3 m) yet relatively high wave energy.

Summary

- Coastal transport processes include solution, suspension, saltation and traction, including longshore drift. The mode of transport for a sediment grain is determined by the size of the grain and the speed of the currents.
- Longshore drift occurs where waves, influenced by prevailing winds, move material along the shoreline. The swash pushes pebbles and sand up onto the beach diagonally, while the backwash moves back towards the sea at right angles, carrying some material with it.
- Processes of coastal deposition result from reduced energy levels and include flocculation and sediment sorting. Sediment is deposited according to its size.
- Depositional coastal landforms include beaches, spits, bars, barrier islands, tombolos and cuspate forelands.
- Beaches are composed of loose, unconsolidated material and adjust their dynamic equilibrium to different conditions.

■ Non-marine influences on the formation of landforms in coastal environments

Aeolian (wind) processes in sand dunes

Coastal sand dunes are common features of many coasts especially in mid latitudes. Excellent examples are found along the Netherlands coast, Les Landes in southwest France and in parts of the UK.

Dunes develop above high tide level and can extend several kilometres inland. Some dune systems consist of a sequence of ridges and troughs parallel to the shore, whereas others are more complex dune fields with some ridges at right angles to the sea. The height of the dune ridges varies from 1–2 m up to 30–40 m above sea level. Optimum conditions for a dune system to form are:

- an abundant supply of sand, usually sourced from the sea bed
- a low beach gradient
- a macro-tidal range that exposes a large area of beach for reworking
- strong prevailing onshore winds
- an area of 'inland space' for the dunes to develop on
- vegetation, such as sea couch and marram grass, to colonise the dunes once they have formed

The initial movement of sand by wind occurs when critical wind velocity is attained relative to a given sediment particle size (threshold velocity). Once the initial sand movement occurs and the particles are entrained, transport occurs, with the most common process being **saltation**. For sand to be deposited again, a reduction in wind velocity is needed, for example in the lee of obstacles or the frictional impact of vegetation. Sand then accumulates quickly to form a streamlined dune form with a gently sloping upward (stoss) side and steeper gradient downwind (lee) side. A single foredune ridge is the basic requirement for the establishment of a coastal dune system, dependent on the availability of further sediment supply from the source beach.

- If sediment supply is low then sand blown inland from the foredune may not be replaced, rendering the dune vulnerable to storm erosion and **blowouts** by **deflation** of winds — loose sand may be reformed as **parabolic dunes** behind the blowout.
- Foredune morphology will be maintained if the loss of sand from the system is matched by new supplies from the beach.
- Where sediment supply from the beach exceeds that lost from the foredune (net sediment gain) a whole series of dune ridges may be formed. Dunes usually begin to form above the spring high tide level.

If **pioneer** plant species — i.e. those that can survive scarcity of water, mobile land surfaces, high levels of salt, exposure to strong winds and a low level of nutrients — establish themselves (such as sand twitch or sea couch grass), frictional drag from the stems and leaves of the plants reduces wind speed, allowing sand to accumulate.

Marram grass and roots also trap sand and, initially, small low embryo dunes develop. If sufficient sand accumulates, adjacent embryo dunes merge to form a line of foredunes, which develop into sizeable ridges and are colonised by vegetation. Migration landward of new yellow dunes occurs when saturated sand grains move up and over the ridge and are deposited on the lee slope, up to a rate of 5–7 m per year. Ultimately, older grey dunes, a long way from the sea, become fixed as they are covered by vegetation.

Knowledge check 11

Define 'saltation' and explain why it is the most common means of transport in sand dune formation.

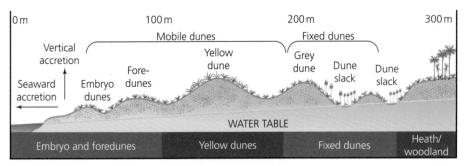

Figure 13 Sand dune zonation

A sequence of parallel ridges can then develop, extending inland (see Figure 13). Between the ridges, hollows known as **slacks** are found. As soon as the wind crosses a ridge, its speed at ground level initially falls, then increases again towards the bottom of the lee slope, so eroding the slack, which may contain water. If the wind drills down to the water table, especially in winter when rainfall is usually high, a lagoon is formed. Many dunes contain blowouts. These are initiated by the removal of significant amounts of vegetation by human and animal activity, which leads to the wind removing the sand by deflation. This is an example of a **positive feedback**, as shown below.

→ loss of vegetation → sand removal → increased wind speed as less friction from plants → more mobile sand → greater difficulty of vegetation re-establishment

Fluvial processes in estuarine environments

Both estuaries and deltas are locations where rivers extend into the coastal zone. They result from interaction between marine and fluvial processes, i.e. salt water and fresh water. The degree of mixing of fresh water and salt water in an estuary influences ecosystem development.

The sediments found in an estuary come from three different sources:

1 fluvial/glacial land-based sources
2 estuary margin sources
3 sources outside the estuary itself, for example from longshore drift or cliff erosion downdrift from the estuary mouth

In the low energy environment of an estuary the dominant process is deposition, so the estuary can be regarded as a sediment sink for sand and mud.

Tidal flats

Around the edges of estuaries, extensive unvegetated depositional areas are found, known as **tidal mudflats**. These are intertidal areas. At low tide intricate patterns of channels and rills are exposed. Most mudflats are a mixture of sand and mud, for example Afon Mawddach near Barmouth on the west coast of Wales, but they do show some zoning as a result of sorting.

In terms of energy input, the outer (seaward) part of the estuary receives much tidal and wave energy, while the inner (landward) part of the estuary has considerable energy inputs from river currents. The result is that finer sediments (mud) are transported through these two areas, into the 'less energetic' central zone where they are deposited. The coarser sands tend to be deposited in the inner and outer parts of the estuary in the more energetic zones.

Tidal mudflats provide ideal environments for organisms such as lugworms ('the fisherman's friend'), which churn up the tidal mudflats by burrowing, a process known as **bioturbation**.

Salt marshes

Salt marshes usually exist in protected, sheltered environments including behind spits and bars, and along the fringes of estuaries as well as open coastlines.

At a macro-scale, a salt marsh coastal system appears as a near-horizontal platform that slopes gently seaward, but at a micro-scale a wide variety of features, such as channels, rills and salt pans can be seen concentrated around tidal creeks.

The platforms are built up by the deposition of sediment brought on to the marsh surface by flood tide currents, and then trapped by vegetation. Sediment **accretion** therefore leads to platform elevation. As the rate of sediment accretion is greater in the lower part of the platform, the lower marsh areas are elevated at a faster rate, making the platform almost horizontal over time.

Like sand dunes, salt marshes result from the interaction of geomorphological and ecological processes. The key to their formation is a low energy tidal environment, where the sea's erosional ability is limited, permitting plant colonisation and sediment accretion.

Salt marshes are both complex and fragile. Like many other coastal sedimentary systems, salt marshes are extremely sensitive to changing environmental conditions that affect the rates of sediment accretion or the level of erosive processes. The environmental changes may be natural, such as the impact of rising levels or storms, or human induced, such as the impact of draining and land reclamation or the accidental introduction of spartina grass (an invasive or alien species). Salt marshes are threatened by a huge range of factors, but they are so valuable in the goods and services they provide that there are many management plans in place to conserve them. As a result of a coastal management strategy of managed realignment, new salt marshes are being artificially created (see p. 46).

(see p. 46)

Biotic processes in mangroves and coral reefs

Mangroves

The principal difference between salt marshes and mangroves is the greater above-ground biomass in mangroves. There are many different species of mangrove trees, all of which can tolerate relatively high levels of salt in the water. They are restricted to a zone of about 30° either side of the Equator. Mangroves have multiple aerial tap roots that emerge from the trunk, above the mud, which anchor the tree, help with oxygen uptake and assist in the trapping of sediment (so mangroves are an important sediment store). As occurs on tidal mudflats, **flocculation** of fine particles is a key process. In a mangrove forest (mangal) zonation occurs.

Knowledge check 12

Draw a spider diagram to summarise the physical and human factors that affect salt marsh development.

Exam tip

Obtain a map of the global distribution of both mangroves and coral reefs so that you can locate named areas.

Coral reefs

A coral reef coast is an example of a rocky coast. Coral coastlines are found in about 100 countries and are grouped into three main formations geographically: the Indo-Pacific formation, the Western Atlantic formation and the smaller Red Sea formation.

Coral reefs build up over time, as each coral polyp (a small animal with tiny tentacles) secretes a calcareous skeleton that it leaves behind when it dies. Growth rates are usually 1–100 cm per year and reefs eventually achieve a thickness of hundreds of metres. Coral polyps have a symbiotic relationship with tiny algae known as **zooxanthellae**. The ideal conditions for coral growth are:

■ clear sea to allow light penetration (avoidance of silted areas such as river mouths)
■ tropical water temperatures of between 23°C and 29°C
■ sea salinity of between 30 ppt and 40 ppt
■ shallow water no deeper than 100 m
■ well-aerated water, resulting from relatively strong wave activity

Dead coral is susceptible to erosion by wave activity, which can reduce the coral limestone to rubble that may be transported by tidal currents to infill active reef structures, to create rubble mounds suitable for new coral colonisation, or to be swept into a pile to create coral islands (cays and motus).

The morphology of reefs usually comprises a 'fetch-facing' outer windward side, which is eroded by the breaking waves, and a relatively protected 'leeward' side where new coral colonies are developing. Debris from the eroded windward side is often deposited on the 'platform' surface, graded from coarse to fine debris towards the lee side. Wave refraction contributes to the piling up of debris to begin the process of **cay** formation.

Summary

■ Non-marine influences in coastal environments include wind action, river action and biotic processes.
■ Sand dune formation requires a supply of sand, a low beach gradient, a large area of exposed beach, strong prevailing onshore winds, an area for the dunes to develop in and vegetation to colonise the dunes once they have formed.
■ Sand dunes begin to be formed when wind speed is sufficient to move sediment of a given particle size. Particles are commonly transported by saltation and deposited once the wind speed drops.
■ Fluvial processes in estuarine environments form tidal flats, salt marshes and micro-features such as channels and rills.
■ Tidal flats are extensive, unvegetated intertidal areas. Salt marsh coastal systems form a near-horizontal platform sloping gently seaward, with micro-features such as channels, rills and salt pans around tidal creeks.
■ Salt marshes are built up by the deposition of sediment (accretion) brought by flood tide currents and trapped by vegetation in a process of succession.
■ Biotic processes influence the development of coral reefs and mangrove coastlines in mostly tropical locations.

■ Variations in coastal processes, landforms and landscapes over different timescales

Table 5 shows the scale of coastal changes in relation to both absolute and human timescales.

Table 5 The scale of coastal changes over time

Absolute timescale	Human timescale	Coastal process
Seconds Minutes Hours Days Weeks Months Years	Dumping of litter, sewage Emergency defences against erosion and floods Impacts of tourists, visitors and local population Coastal management decisions Coastal development	Sediment movement by wind or water Cliff falls from mass movements Tidal cycles, shore normal sediment movement. Storms Storm surges, breaks of defences Beach scour Shore profile adjustment Tidal cycles Shore profile adjustment (seasonal) Coast accretion erosion Coastal process response to defences Longshore drift
Decades	Coastal defences	Erosion and accretion cycles Coastal process response to defences Formation and loss of habitat
Centuries	Shifts in settlement	Historic coastal development, loss of towns and villages to the sea
Millennia		Sea level changes in response to glaciation, tectonics etc.

Increasing timescale (left margin, indicating downward direction)

Rapid process and landform change

High energy storm events and the resulting erosion of beaches and dunes, and the rapid mass movement processes in cliffs can take place over a very short time span, literally from seconds to hours and certainly over a day.

Storm-generated erosion

Storm-generated erosion can occur on very short timescales. At midday on Monday 26 February 1990, a violent storm breached the sea wall at Towyn, North Wales, flooding 10 km^2 of low-lying land, damaging 2800 houses and 6000 caravans. The Towyn floods were caused by a cocktail of **physical factors**. A particularly deep depression caused a storm surge 1.3 m high that combined with extremely high spring tides and strong 130 km h^{-1} onshore winds and led to overtopping of the sea wall (a 1 in 200 year event). Huge volumes of seawater spilled through the gap, flooding the pumping stations that drain the land used for farming. **Human factors**, such as failure to repair the sea wall and the fact that the embankment had not been improved to be future-proof against rising sea levels, exacerbated the floods. Usually, new development triggers sea wall defence improvements. However, although there had been recent large-scale development of retirement bungalows and holiday parks, supported by planning permission, on these very low-lying areas at Towyn,

> **Exam tip**
>
> Always keep your case studies up to date using the internet.

unfortunately the upgrade to the sea defences that was due had not been carried out. The actual breach of the sea wall happened in around an hour and flooding occurred rapidly over a wide area, augmented by river flooding.

Worldwide, much of the severe coastal damage comes from hurricanes, typhoons and cyclones, i.e. tropical storms such as Hurricane Katrina, Gulf coast, USA (2005) and Typhoon Haiyan in the Philippines (2013). The impact from a tropical storm is felt over a number of days as the storm migrates, with any one area usually affected for 1–3 days.

Changes at a seasonal temporal scale

There is a strong relationship between waves (in particular wave steepness) and the angle of beach profile. Wave steepness is the ratio of wave height to wave length — the higher the value, the greater the energy brought by the wave onto the beach.

As Figure 14 shows, there are seasonal changes in the angle of the beach profile. The beach is in short-term equilibrium with the contrasting seasonal conditions.

In winter the waves tend to have more energy (generally stronger winds) so they erode and transport sediment offshore, possibly forming an offshore bar, so lowering the beach profile. During summer, the waves are generally less energetic, so they move material onshore, building the beach up.

Tides also have an impact on beach profile. In areas of monsoonal or other markedly seasonal climate in terms of rainfall, the wet and dry seasons show clear beach profile changes too.

A further complication is the influence of the beach steepness on the waves. On a steep beach waves tend to be plunging, and a significant amount of the incoming energy is reflected back from the beach (known as a **reflective** beach). Conversely, on a shallow-angled beach the waves break and spill as the wave base is reached further out from the shore, so dissipating the wave energy as the waves move across the wide beach (known as a **dissipative** beach).

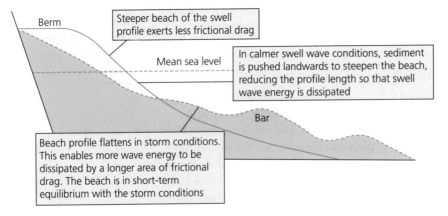

Figure 14 Seasonal changes in beach profiles

The calibre (size) of the beach material can also affect the angle of steepness, with steeper beaches being associated with larger sediment and shallower beaches being associated with fine-grained sediment. The link between sediment size and beach gradient is thus a result of contrasting **percolation** rates. Moreover, particle size affects the angle of rest — the larger the particle size, the steeper the angle of rest.

Process and landform changes over millennia

Sea level is continuously changing. Globally, all coasts have undergone considerable variations in sea level over geological time and especially since the Quaternary period, beginning about 2 million years ago. Some coastlines have experienced more 'recent' sea level change than others. Since the last extensive glaciation, sea levels have risen by about 120 m.

Changes in sea level alter energy inputs and outputs and are therefore important for the development of landforms.

Causes of sea level change

Eustatic changes involve changes in **absolute** sea levels and are **global** because all oceans and seas are interconnected. While the total volume of water in the global hydrological cycle (a closed system) is constant, changes in where and how water is stored cause eustatic change.

Eustatic changes are therefore unrelated to local/regional effects. They are most commonly caused by changes in the ocean water volume and temperature (thermal expansion and contraction of the ocean). As oceans cool their volume contracts and when they warm it expands. While this is a worldwide change the impact is more marked in tropical oceans. Similarly a decrease in salinity will cause a rise in sea level and vice versa. These changes in salinity and temperature are believed to make a difference of only about 10 m to global sea levels, and so are of much less significant than changes in sea level associated with the accumulation or melting of ice. These are **glacio-eustatic changes** which occur when ice on continental ice caps and ice sheets forms and melts, taking ice from or releasing it back into the oceans. (Note that the increase and decline in the size and amount of floating sea ice, including ice bergs, ice shelves and ice pack, has **no** influence on sea level. This is because ice will displace the equivalent of its own mass.)

It is estimated that if the Greenland and Antarctic ice sheets melted there would be a eustatic sea level rise of up to 90 m. However, sinking of the ocean basins under the influence of the weight of all the water (hydro-isostasy) would diminish the impact (negative feedback) to around 60 m.

Isostatic sea level changes are **regional** changes of sea level. The Earth's crust 'floats' on a denser underlying layer (asthenosphere). This two-layer system is in isostatic balance when the total weight of the crust is exactly balanced by its buoyancy. The addition of a load at a particular point of the crust (which could be water, ice or increasing sediment from a large delta) will upset this equilibrium. To compensate for the increased coastal weight, some of the asthenosphere will flow away, causing isostatic depression as the land level falls.

Isostatic readjustment or **rebound** will occur, for example, when the ice sheet melts and the land reverts back to its former position.

Figure 15 shows the complex relationship between sea level changes and their impact on landforms.

Knowledge check 14

Distinguish between eustatic and isostatic changes in sea level.

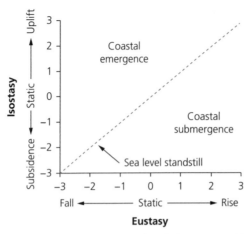

Figure 15 Relationship between sea level changes and landforms

Glacio-isostasy occurs when glaciated continents are depressed by the weight of their glaciers. During glacial periods ocean water volumes and global sea levels are low, but glaciated continents are regionally depressed by the weight of glaciers so their **relative** sea level is higher than that experienced on non-glaciated continents. Upon deglaciation, the removal of the weight of ice causes isostatic rebound or recovery of the land, as is apparent along the coasts of Scotland and the Gulf of Bothnia.

Hydro-isostasy occurs when the volume of water released into an ocean basin exerts a weight onto the ocean floor and depresses it by an amount roughly equivalent to one-third of the depth of the additional water.

In terms of landform formation, sea level changes can be classified as **negative** where there is a relative fall in sea level (i.e. a marine regression). An **emergent** coastline then results, with the coastline building out from its previous position. There are three possible scenarios for a relative fall in sea level.

1 The sea level falls and land either rises, stays still or subsides at a slower pace.
2 The sea level remains fixed while the land rises.
3 The sea level rises but the land rises at a greater pace, e.g. northwest Scotland, which is experiencing a post-glacial rise in sea level, but with a rapid isostatic recovery.

Positive sea level change occurs where there is a relative rise in sea level (i.e. a marine transgression) and a **submerged** coastline results, leading to drowning of the coast and the inshore migration of some landforms, for example beaches. For a relative rise in sea level there are again three possible scenarios.

1 The sea level rises and land either subsides, stays still or rises at a slower pace.
2 The sea level remains fixed while the land subsides.
3 The sea level falls, and the land subsides at a greater pace.

A number of factors influence the landforms produced by changes of sea level as well as the sea level change itself:

- the structure of the coast, whether concordant or discordant (see p. 23)
- the relief of the coast, whether highland or lowland
- special factors, such as whether the coast was glaciated or not before the sea level change

Exam tip

This is a complex area. Try to understand it using simple diagrams. Think of relative sea level rise and positive and negative impacts.

Exam tip

For the Eduqas or WJEC exams you only need to learn about **either** isostatic **or** eustatic changes in sea level, but an understanding of both is relevant for understanding the resulting landform formation.

Emergent landforms

Emerged coastlines are evident when beach deposits and marine shells, for example the patella (limpet) shells on the raised beaches along the Gower Coast, are found stranded above the present-day high tide level, creating a **raised beach** that is often backed by **relict** or fossil cliffs. These beach deposits and shell beds were formed when the sea was at a previously higher level.

The raised shore platform creates a **marine terrace**, an area of flat land which can be utilised for farming as the soils are relatively sandy, or for communications. The presence of a raised platform indicates that, before the relative fall in sea level, the sea must have been at a higher level for a considerable period of time to have allowed the shore platform to develop. Relict cliffs can be identified by a marked break in slope, but they can show signs of degradation from subaerial processes.

Sometimes, as in western Scotland where raised beaches have been identified at 8 m, 15 m and 30 m above present-day sea level, there are a **series** of terraces and relict cliffs. An analysis of the raised beach deposits shows how they have been rounded by corrasion and attrition. Sometimes, fossil sand dunes may also be found high above current sea levels. Associated with the relict cliffs it is possible to find relict caves (Kings Cave, Arran or Paviland Cave, Gower) and sea stacks.

The extent to which raised beaches and their landforms remain intact often depends on their geology and subsequent level of resistance to denudation, as well as their age.

Submergent landforms

Positive changes in sea level mean that the overall shape of the coastline is changed as river and glaciated valleys and coasts are drowned, creating an indented coast of inlets (e.g. rias and fjords), bays and promontories. The sea may also isolate some areas of land to form islands. For example, during the Holocene Flandrian transgression, Great Britain became physically separated from Europe.

Rias

Rias are more common along **discordant** coastlines, where geological strata trend at right angles to non-glaciated coastlines. When global sea levels were lower than at present, base level was lowered, giving rivers a renewed energy to cut downward — forming deep rejuvenated river valleys. Once sea levels began to rise again, drowned river valleys with their winding dendritic pattern, were formed. Rias are tidal, and their central deepwater channels are of vital importance for ports, for example the oil/gas terminals at Milford Haven in southwest Wales (see Figure 16).

Rias are found around the world and examples include those of southern Cornwall and Devon, as well as Galicia on the Iberian Peninsula.

Features similar to rias are formed on **concordant** coastlines where geological strata, mountains, valleys and rivers all trend parallel to the shore, for example on the Dalmatian coast of Croatia. Wide, open bodies of water called **sounds** develop, which have longitudinal islands and ridges of raised land between them.

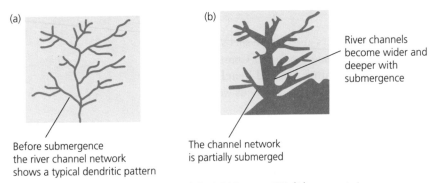

(a)

Before submergence
the river channel network
shows a typical dendritic pattern

(b)

River channels
become wider and
deeper with
submergence

The channel network
is partially submerged

Figure 16 A typical ria (a) 18,000 years BP, (b) present day

Fjords

Fjords (or fiords), sometimes known as sea lochs, are **drowned glacial valleys** which have been shaped by the action of ice and submerged during the Holocene. The deep, steep-sided troughs carved out by moving ice are submerged as sea levels rise. Fjords are formed at higher altitudes where the effects of ice have been more profound. In some upland coastal areas they can reach in excess of 1200 m in depth. Fjords have steep sides and flat bottoms, typical of the U-shaped valleys of glaciated landscapes. They are relatively straight-sided and narrow compared with rias. Also typical of glaciated areas, fjords may have hanging valleys and waterfalls. Ridges of scree and moraine may also line the fjord's shores, providing evidence of its glacial heritage. Fjords have a shallow entrance called a **threshold**. The threshold is occasionally less than 100 m in depth. If the threshold appears at the water's surface it may manifest as islands called skerries (a **skerry** is a small rocky outcrop). The threshold could be a large terminal moraine — material 'bulldozed' by the moving glacier, marking its furthest point of advance during the glacial period — or it could be the point where the glacier's snout was thinner, or perhaps where the glacier began to float, giving the glacier reduced erosive power (see Figure 17).

Knowledge check 15

Explain how you would distinguish between a ria and a fjord.

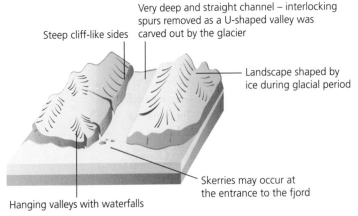

Steep cliff-like sides

Very deep and straight channel – interlocking spurs removed as a U-shaped valley was carved out by the glacier

Landscape shaped by ice during glacial period

Skerries may occur at the entrance to the fjord

Hanging valleys with waterfalls

Figure 17 The key features of fjords after submergence

Exam tip

For Eduqas and WJEC specifications you must select **one** landform and explain the impact of changes of sea level on its formation. Rias, fjords or raised beaches would all be a good choice.

Examples of fjords can be seen often in high latitude locations, such as Sognefjord in Norway, British Columbia in North America, southern Chile and western Scotland.

Summary

- High energy storm events, the resulting erosion of beaches and dunes, and rapid mass movement processes in cliffs can take place in a very short time span, from seconds to hours or over a day.
- In winter waves tend to have more energy because of stronger winds, so they erode and transport sediment offshore, lowering the beach profile. During summer, waves are less energetic, so they move material onshore, building the beach into a steeper profile.
- Changes in sea level alter energy inputs and outputs and influence the development of landforms. Over millennia, all coasts have undergone variations in sea level but some coastlines have experienced more 'recent' sea level change than others.
- Eustatic changes involve changes in absolute sea levels and are global because all oceans and seas are interconnected, but changes in where and how water is stored causes eustatic change. In contrast, isostatic sea level changes are regional and caused by movements of particular parts of the Earth's crust. You will need to know about the impact of these processes on *one* landform.

Coastal processes are a vital context for human activity

Positive impacts of coastal processes on human activity

The coastal zone attracts a range of human activities, especially landward of the high tide level where many land uses are attracted by the potential of low-lying, flat land in a pleasant environment. Other activities such as tourism, fishing and port development are attracted to the intertidal and offshore zones.

Of the inhabited continents, only in Africa do more people live in the interior than in the coastal zone. In Asian countries over 1.5 billion people live within 100 km of the sea. By 2025, about 75% of the residents of the USA are expected to live in coastal areas, which together only accounts for 17% of the land area, with Florida and California leading the way. In many parts of the world the coast is a very crowded zone — for example in China, where coastal population densities average 600 persons km^{-2}.

In the USA, China and most of Latin America more than 70% of major cities are coastally located.

The growth of tourism

Over the past 200 years tourism and recreation have developed into major economic activities along the coast.

By the end of the nineteenth century, in most developed countries seaside holidays were part of the annual rhythm of people's lives, hence the rise of the British seaside resort. As transport has become increasingly sophisticated and journey times

Knowledge check 16

Explain why high latitude coasts are sparsely populated.

Exam tip

Locate the world's major urban agglomerations on a map and notice how many occupy sites on or close to the coast.

dramatically reduced, global travel has become a reality for large numbers of people, as they acquire both the time and money to travel. Coastal areas play a significant role in the global explosion of tourism.

There are certain key resources necessary for the development of coastal resources for tourism and recreation.

Physical resources include attractive coastal scenery (e.g. cliffs) and ecosystems (e.g. corals), sandy beaches, high quality seawater that is free of strong currents and at a pleasant temperature, sunny climates. Different combinations of these physical resources can result in different types of tourism. Well-known examples of world class beaches include those in Florida and the Mediterranean.

As well as physical resources, tourism also needs **human resources**, for example cultural attractions, heritage resources and quality provision of services, accessibility and opportunities for recreational activities. Dubai is an example of a coastally located area that has many artificial attractions which have made it one of the fastest growing tourist destinations in the world.

While there are numerous references to the negative environmental impacts of tourism these have to be counterbalanced by the positive impacts, both economically and socially.

Coastal tourism aids economic development in a number of ways. Foreign exchange earnings can be enhanced by levying taxes such as tourist and airport tax. For developing nations, construction of hotels and resorts has such high capital costs that it can only happen if there is inward investment (FDI) from countries such as China, the UK and Japan. The trend in tourism, as in other service industries, is towards greater **globalisation** of operations. Hence, large transnational corporations (TNCs) are increasingly involved, often acting as conglomerates, with shares in hotels, airlines and leisure developments.

Tourism is the world's largest employer, with an enormous range of jobs available. There is a small core labour force of full-time highly paid professionals, supported by a large number of workers, often poorly paid, who are engaged in low-cost labour-intensive functions, such as cleaning. Often, the better jobs do not go to local people, but this is being remedied by training programmes. There are also plentiful opportunities for local entrepreneurs, for example in craft industries or personal services such as guiding. The diversity of employment opportunities acts as a magnet for local people, for example Ecuadoreans drawn to the opportunities provided by tourism in the Galapagos.

Tourism also generates its own **multiplier effects**. Essentially, as a resort develops, often in a tourism enclave, so does the local economy. As profits from tourism increase and become more widespread, so they begin to **trickle down** into the local economy. In theory, the multiplier effect should lead to the emergence of more local suppliers and a decreasing reliance on foreign imports.

The multiplier effect can improve the quality of local services for local people, as the people employed in tourism will have money to spend and for investment. For example, in some islands in the Maldives, restaurant workers are investing in small hotels that employ both local workers and migrant labour from Bangladesh, at both the construction and operation stages.

The strength of the multiplier effect and the magnitude of its economic impact vary according to a range of factors:

- the **level of development** of the local economy, i.e. what it can supply for the expansion of tourism (goods and services) and to meet tourists' needs
- the **type of tourism:** in theory, elite tourists should spend more, but this is not the case if they are on **all-inclusive** deals
- the **organisation of tourism:** cruise ships are a contentious issue as it is not clear how much this type of tourism puts back into the local economy
- the **level of leakage**, i.e. losses of income to foreign countries, for example, when brandy is imported or multi-national hotels send all their profits back to headquarters in a developed country

Whether the impacts of tourism are really positive is contentious, environmentally, economically and socio-culturally. It can be argued that the investment in people and places is positive because money earned can be used to improve both physical and human coastal environments, for example by replanting coastal wetlands or recharging the sand on beaches, as well as providing high quality facilities. So much depends on the scale and pace of tourism development, and how well the tourism is managed to take care of the environment and support local culture.

Negative impacts of coastal processes on human activity

A number of factors influence the rate of erosion on all types of coast (see p. 21). Erosion rarely occurs at a steady rate, and usually happens dramatically after a severe storm. These major events, often with a recurrence level of 1 in 100, can dramatically upset the dynamic equilibrium and lead to extensive cliff retreat or massive beach erosion (see p. 34). Eustatic rises in sea level associated with global warming and the melting of ice sheets will mean that the impacts of storms are increasingly felt further inland.

Coastal erosion can be exacerbated by inappropriate coastal development too near the shore or by coastal management. Many sites of dramatic change occur downdrift from newly constructed jetties or hard engineering defences, which cause sediment starvation.

The more high value and high density the land development, the greater the economic losses associated with coastal erosion. The website www.coastalwatch. com assesses the variable impact of coastal erosion round the coasts of Australia. **Cost–benefit** analysis is key to understanding what action, if any, should be taken to manage coastal erosion.

The overall economic and social impacts of coastal erosion are generally negative:

- danger to life, in particular from sudden landslides and rock falls from cliffs, e.g. along the Dorset coast
- structural damage to buildings and infrastructure, e.g. along the Holderness coast of Yorkshire
- damage and destruction to lifeline infrastructure such as water, sewage and gas pipes, as on the Louisiana coast in the USA
- loss of land which may profitably be used for farming (e.g. Sue Earl's Farm on the Holderness coast)

Knowledge check 17

Explain what is meant by a recurrence level of 1 in 100.

- loss of vulnerable ecosystems (e.g. in the Louisiana wetlands) which have high recreational and tourism value, e.g. as bird reserves, and impacts on valuable coastal fisheries
- local instability of nearby areas, which can result in huge declines in property values, for both residential and holiday amenities, as well as psychological stress for residents and owners who face financial ruin — owners may have to accept **red lining** strategies that restrict development seaward of or near the red line (e.g. Norfolk coast) and may make assets uninsurable
- beach erosion will lead to loss of beach amenity, a major problem for many holiday resorts as the lack of a beach will have huge knock-on effects on their ability to profit from tourism

Strategies to manage the impacts of coastal processes on human activity

The concept of protecting the coast is a contested one. Contrasting opinions arise — from the concerns of industry, tourism and residential sectors who see a need to 'hold the sea in place' and prevent it encroaching on the land, through to environmentalists and coastal planners who favour leaving the coast in as natural a state as possible.

There are five generic strategies for coastal management.

1 **Do nothing**, with no protection, which would lead to eventual abandonment.
2 **Managed retreat or realignment**, which plans for retreat using engineering solutions that recognise the natural processes of adjustment yet identify a new line of defence.
3 **Hold the line**, which favours shoreline protection by defence from hard engineering structures such as sea walls, often supported by other methods such as groynes or beach nourishment.
4 **Move seawards** or **advance** by constructing new defences such as offshore breakwaters seaward of original defences.
5 **Limited intervention**, which involves accommodation, by which adjustments are made to allow coping with inundation from rising sea levels by raising coastal land and building vertically, combined with state-sponsored insurance at affordable costs.

The choice of strategy or strategies is site-specific and depends on a number of factors.

Physical factors concerning the nature of the coast itself:
- the coastal geomorphology, such as the hardness of the rock and the amount of sediment supplied by erosion (e.g. from soft rocks such as sand and clay)
- the degree of dynamism in the coastal environment, such as erosion rates, or pattern of sea level change and the precise nature of the coastal problem to be managed (whether flooding or erosion)
- the quality of the natural coastal environment, e.g. high value ecosystems with rare flora and fauna; in some beautiful environments hard engineering defences would be an eyesore.

Exam tip

While case studies are important, they need to be used to support a line of argument by adaptation.

Knowledge check 18

Explain the circumstances under which the rare option of 'advance the existing coastline seawards' might be taken.

There are also **financial** and **political considerations**. Of fundamental importance is the principle of **cost–benefit analysis**, as there is a need to balance the high overall costs of coastal defences against the benefits of protection, which depends on the calculated value of all the coastal development. In economic terms, expensive hard engineering defences are only worthwhile to protect and defend areas of high value coastal developments.

Table 6 summarises the costs of coastal defences in 2015.

Table 6 Costs of coastal defences, 2015

Sea walls	Approximately £5000 per metre for basic type
Timber revetment	Approximately £1500 per metre
Rip rap	£1000–3000 per metre
Gabions	£45–50 per m³ (cubic metre)
Timber groyne	£1000 per metre, average length 100 m, cost per groyne = £100,000
Beach nourishment	£10 per m³ — thousands of metric loads needed for most large schemes
Offshore breakwater	Millions of pounds — usually costs £10–30 million

In **political** terms there are tensions between national government's overall budget spending and local government. For many coastal communities coastal defence is seen as imperative at all costs as, ultimately, without coastal defences settlements will be inundated by storm surges or washed away by erosion.

Until recently, in many coastal areas there has been limited expenditure on scientific research, so the dynamics of coastal processes have been imperfectly understood.

Socio-cultural factors are also significant. Surveys have shown that many coastal residents and business owners do not feel safe unless they are protected by obvious sea wall style defences.

There are three *broad* management strategies that can be used:

1 cliff face strategies
2 cliff foot strategies
3 beach management strategies

This guide will look at cliff face strategies, but the other two would also give you plenty of scope.

> **Exam tip**
>
> Beware of discussing just one strategy, such as building sea walls, as this gives your knowledge an overly narrow base. Another way of tackling this topic would be researching either hard or soft management strategies and selecting one of the five generic shoreline management options, such as 'hold the line' (see p. 42).

Table 7 summarises the benefits and problems of cliff face strategies. Recommended use of such strategies is restricted to areas of high risk, where alternative sediment supplies are available to compensate for losses from cliffs, and where cliff-top development is too valuable to allow cliff failure.

> **Exam tip**
>
> Note that for WJEC and Eduqas you have to select *one* management strategy to manage the impacts of coastal processes on human activity.

> **Exam tip**
>
> Always support the strategies you describe with detailed examples.

Table 7 Benefits and problems of cliff face strategies

Benefits	Problems
■ Increased security for cliff-top developments ■ Increased security for beach users ■ Increased security for coastal towns ■ Can be environmentally attractive, especially where vegetated ■ Avoids compensation issues that would be caused by 'do nothing'	■ Reduced sediment supply from subaerial sources to coastal sediment budget ■ Reduced exposure for scientific study (geology/palaeontology etc.) ■ Costs do not always justify the results, which must always be supported by detailed research of marine and subaerial processes

Case study

One management strategy to manage the impacts of coastal processes on human activity

Controlling subaerial erosion to prevent cliff retreat (cliff face strategies)

Cliffs vary in their lithology and structure and so fail in many different ways. In an ideal situation it is preferable not to defend cliffs as the sediment they supply is a vital component of the sediment system. However, people who live on top of cliffs feel entitled to some form of protection against cliff recession, which may average up to 20 m per year for cliffs of unconsolidated sands.

One future-proofing system is to use the concept of **red lining**, where the rate of cliff retreat is modelled and any development seaward of a specified line is prevented. The coastline in the USA is classified according to its modelled 'life expectancy' and this controls decisions on development.

Cliff failure tends to be episodic, with dramatic changes after winter storms which can combine with high tides and storm surges resulting from various types of mass movement (rock falls, rotational slippage, mud slides and mud flows, and toppling) (see p. 19). A number of strategies exist, which are frequently combined with cliff foot strategies for protection of the cliff toe.

- **Pinning** involves inserting bolts or pins through the likely shear planes, as has been done at the White Cliffs of Dover where the cliffs themselves are a World Heritage Site.
- **Grading** involves decreasing both the height and slope angle of the cliffs to reduce the threat of mass movement and to stabilise the cliff face. At

Llantwit Major in South Wales, rock falls from horizontally bedded limestones underlain by relatively weak shales were causing danger to recreational users. The upper cliff was blasted in 1969 to reduce its slope angle, and the blast material used as armouring to protect the cliff toe. However, the blasting weakened the rock and allowed increased weathering and the cliff remained geologically unstable, so the scheme was considered unsuccessful.

- **Cliff drainage** is a common practice, especially for cliffs with a high clay content. Pore water pressures can be reduced by drainage lines in the cliff face, field drains, gravel trenches and by intercepting overland flow. However, this can result in subsidence of cliff-top land as the cliff dries out, and it can also have an ecological impact.
- **Gabions** (steel wire baskets about 2 m × 1 m in size, filled with rock) are used to stabilise the cliff 'toe' and help cliff drainage, especially behind a sea wall.
- **Vegetation** planting and fencing cliff faces can increase slope stability after grading. At Bournemouth the sand and clay cliffs have been planted with privet hedges and shrubs, and seeded with grasses and other ground cover. This improves the appearance of the cliff face and contributes to the long-term stabilisation of the regraded slope.
- **Toe protection**, by sea walls, revetments or rock armour and beach feeding, often works in tandem with cliff face strategies, especially where the land is of high value or the problem is severe.

Summary

- Positive impacts of coastal processes on human activity include the attractive potential of low-lying, flat land and a pleasant environment for settlement and land uses such as agriculture, transport and industry. Activities such as tourism, fishing and port development are attracted to intertidal and offshore zones. Many major cities have grown from ports, with resulting high populations in coastal zones.
- Tourism, often located in coastal environments, requires both physical and human resources and is now a major global industry. Tourism development has a multiplier effect on the local economy.
- The impact of storms and coastal erosion have a negative effect, causing social and economic losses such as danger to life, structural damage to buildings and infrastructure (e.g. water, sewage, gas pipes), loss of land for farming, loss of ecosystems with high recreational and tourism value, impacts on valuable coastal fisheries, instability of nearby areas, psychological stress for residents, and loss of beach amenities and tourism.
- Strategies to manage the impacts of coastal processes on human activity include: do nothing, managed retreat or realignment, hold the line, move seawards or advance by constructing new defences, and limited intervention. You will need to know a case study of one management strategy to manage the impacts of coastal processes on human activity.

■ The impact of human activity on coastal landscape systems

Positive impacts of human activity

Human activities, if managed effectively, can have a positive impact on coastal landscape systems. After generations of hard engineering schemes, there has been a move towards softer engineering solutions, which aim to work with the sea as opposed to against it. This section explores managed realignment as an example of how coastal management can have a generally positive impact, with ecological and environmental benefits outweighing some of the problems.

There has also been a rethink of coastal management, with the development of **integrated shoreline management** strategies where the coast is considered holistically and managed sustainably, with humans very much part of the system (see p. 50).

Moreover, in response to an enormous range of pressures on the coast there has been a range of strategies developed to protect the coast and to adopt conservation management plans. Conservation strategies range from total protection through to various forms of sustainable management that allow public access.

Protection strategies operate at a range of scales and have had a positive impact.
- Global frameworks, such as the development of coastal World Heritage Sites, such as parts of the Great Barrier Reef, Australia or the Jurassic Coast of Dorset.
- Establishment of marine reserves at a national scale using an international (World Resources Institute) framework.
- Development of Sites of Special Scientific Interest (SSSIs) such as sand dunes, mangroves or salt marshes at a local scale.

> **Exam tip**
>
> Try to look at example areas outside the UK too, such as the Florida Coastal Management Program which manages the impacts of development in mangroves, seagrass beds and coral, or the Great Barrier Reef Management Plans which give a detailed account of zoning.

In the UK many nature reserves and special conservation areas are excellent topics for fieldwork reports, such as evaluating the need for and success of management plans, e.g. at Whiteford Burrows, Gower, Wales.

Managed coastal realignment

Managed realignment (also called managed natural retreat) means allowing the sea to flood areas that were previously protected. In time, salt marshes and mudflats form a zone that provides a natural defence to the 'new' shore, landwards of the abandoned area.

Managed realignment makes good sense where hinterland usage or development does not prevent it. It provides a way to compensate for the impacts of sea level rise and encourages natural environmental processes. The high and growing cost of schemes to prevent erosion and flooding mean that alternative approaches need to be pioneered. This approach was developed as an option only in the mid 1990s, so coastal managers are still learning about it.

The success or not of particular schemes depends on a complex set of variables:

- estuary size, shape and location
- degree of wave exposure needed to reduce transport of silt from flooded fields
- tidal regime
- current land use and value, as this influences compensation and costs claims
- the land should, once designated, not be farmed using **agrochemicals**
- public perception is that this type of solution is 'giving in to the sea'
- the quality of the chosen site — i.e. its height above sea level, whether it is adjacent to an existing marsh area that can act as a seed bank, has suitable hydrological conditions that can be managed to prevent scouring and allow sufficient water to facilitate sedimentation — otherwise there is potential for failure
- site 'science' well researched, with accurate details and understanding of hydrological sedimentological and ecological processes
- good site management to ensure that the breaches of the existing walls are correctly sited, with relict creek networks present as new man-made channels

The anticipated consequences of such a revolutionary approach are many and generally positive.

- It is more sustainable, producing habitats of high ecological value such as new salt marshes and mudflats.
- It encourages 'natural' protection, e.g. mudflats and salt marshes, to counter **coastal squeeze**.
- It provides a possible reduction in the costs of protection — so much depends on the value of the land (below £18,000 per hectare, with limited coastal settlement and economic activity preferable).

However, these schemes are relatively new so they are controversial and their full impacts are not yet known. Examples include the Essex Coast (e.g. Abbots Hall Farm) and Pagham Harbour (southern England), the North Sea Coast (Netherlands),

Louisiana and Florida (USA). Table 8 assesses the benefits and potential problems of this management option.

Table 8 The benefits and potential problems of managed realignment

Benefits	Potential problems
■ Increased intertidal width and wave attenuation capacity ■ Increased conservation potential as there are additional habitats, many of high quality and ecofriendly ■ Retained naturalness of estuary zones ■ Increased protection against sea level rise and the avoidance of coastal squeeze ■ Potentially a cheaper option as low value land with opportunities for visitor income (e.g. birding at Cley) of up to £40,000 net per year (after maintenance costs)	■ Danger of incorrectly managing and modifying tidal processes ■ Experimental, novel technique which has some potential for failure ■ Complexity of potential compensation issues with farmers — so may have high start-up costs ■ Uncertainty about hydrology and sediment movements and adaptation to rising sea levels. Complex to manage and possibility of disaster ■ While it is an obvious solution and has much to commend it the public have poor perceptions of its value, i.e. 'giving up', 'giving in to the sea' ■ Can only be used in certain estuary sites — not a universal cure ■ May need to be part of a wider estuary scheme rather than a piecemeal small-scale isolated scheme ■ Environmental values can be over-estimated. Impact on shellfish industries still uncertain

Knowledge check 19

Evaluate the extent to which managed realignment has positive impacts as a coastal management option.

Negative impacts of human activity

Several types of human activities are damaging to the coastal environment. The coastal zone is a contested zone, with increasing numbers of people having different opinions on how it should be used, managed, engineered and valued. It is hardly surprising, therefore, that there is conflict between conservation of the environment and the need to develop the coast economically.

Offshore dredging

Dredging for aggregates, sand and gravel takes place at varying scales, from small-scale abstraction to industrial-scale, commercial dredging operations. In most developed countries dredging is licensed as it is a potentially destructive activity to both marine ecosystems and the wider environment. Clark has identified dredging 'as the greatest single threat to coastal ecosystems'. For this reason, in most EU countries and Japan, dredging is restricted to areas landward of the 20 m **isobaths**.

Dredged sand and gravel is used for shoreline protection, where it forms hardcore for offshore breakwaters and other defences as well as being used for beach nourishment. Dredging is also frequently used to improve shipping access to ports or marinas by providing deeper navigable channels for even larger ships. The UK is particularly well-endowed with abundant offshore gravel and sand deposits, as these are relict deposits from the Pleistocene.

Subaqueous dredging has huge impacts on the sea bed. For example, a survey of offshore dredging along the coast of France showed that 160 km² was affected, causing serious ecological damage. The habitats of fish, invertebrates and algae are adversely affected, and benthic (bottom-dwelling) fauna are removed in the process, so disrupting the marine food webs, which in turn impacts on birds and mammals. Many popular dredging areas are the spawning grounds of fish, e.g. Dogger Bank in the North Sea, so resulting in a decline in fish stocks.

In selective dredging, any small-calibre material that is not required is released back into the water. The fine sediment settles back after a long period of time but, in the meantime, the resulting high levels of turbidity suffocate filter feeders such as mussels. As harbours are deepened, surplus mud and other sediments (spoil disposal dumping) are taken out to sea and offloaded on the continental shelf.

Poisons (toxins), such as heavy metals and hydrogen sulphide, may be released from sea bed sediment into the water column when dredging occurs. Nutrients are also released, which can lead to algal blooms.

Other environmental effects relate to the deepening of inshore waters, increasing shore-face slopes, and therefore allowing larger waves to break close inshore, causing increased damage to the coast. Hallsands in Devon is a useful illustration of those impacts.

Knowledge check 20

List the safeguards that can be put in place to manage the impacts of dredging.

Erosion of sand dunes

Sand dunes are dynamic systems, constantly adjusting to variations in wind patterns and sediment supply (p. 29). Their presence and stability is of fundamental importance to coastal protection, for example off the Dutch coast, but they are threatened by human activity.

Dunes are highly fragile environments, formed from uncompacted sediment and poorly bound by vegetation, which, coupled with their exploitation for a variety of activities, makes them vulnerable to damage from overuse and misuse.

Table 9 Categories of human impacts on dunes

Conversion	Removal	Use	External
Urbanisation Golf courses Agriculture Forestry	Mining Development	Tourism Trampling Horse riding Sand yachting Off-road vehicles Water extraction Conservation Military training	Reduced sediment supply Sea defences Dune migration prevention

Human impacts on sand dunes can be grouped into four categories (Table 9).

1 **Conversion** involves changing the vegetation type (e.g. afforestation, agriculture or golf courses) or the nature of the dunes by urbanisation and development. The dunes cease to function in their natural manner, either because sediment cannot be blown inland or because the dunes are built on.

2 **Removal** is where the sand is removed for other uses, e.g. mined for glass making, or when dune profiles are altered to facilitate beach access or provide a sea view.

3 **Utilisation** involves using the current resources. All types of tourism use the dune as an **amenity** with often disastrous effects on 'dune health' if the area is not managed. However, even dune conservation can have a negative impact,

e.g. where blowouts are artificially created to encourage growth of marram grass, as this can lead to escalating rates of destruction.

4 **External** impacts include those from beyond the dune environment. Dunes can only survive with an adequate supply of sediment — any activity that inhibits this, such as building coastal defences, will induce net dune decay, as they lose their ability to build and migrate.

Knowledge check 21

Explain why sand dunes have a low threshold of survival against damaging actions.

Dunes tend to have a low threshold of survival, with only low levels of interference required to induce negative changes.

When development takes place on sand dunes for housing or holiday accommodation, all the available sand is sealed below the tarmac, rendering the dunes immobile. There is a loss of naturalness of the remaining surrounding dunes, and habitat fragmentation and habitat loss also occur. Constant dune encroachment on development triggers further demands for protection, especially from future flooding risks. The dunes suffer knock-on damage from holiday campsites, evening barbeques, general vandalism and overuse by trampling, e.g. at Island Beach, New Jersey, USA. Mechanised sand mining, as on the southern Brittany coast near Morbihan, can lead to dune degradation and erosion as removal takes place at a greater rate than renewal.

Experiments have shown that trampling at even a low level of, say, 150 'passes' (i.e. 75 return journeys) per month can lead to a 50% reduction in vegetation, creating bare ground and the development of blowouts (e.g. South Shore Beach, Blackpool).

Water extraction can lower the water table, thus rendering the dunes more liable to wind erosion. Also, as water is extracted, salt water is drawn in — saline intrusion can damage the dune slacks.

Management strategies can be developed to stabilise and reconstruct the coastal dunes as well as to control usage, although the heavier the usage the more difficult management becomes. There are three approaches.

1 Heavily degraded areas need **complete reconstruction**.
2 On less severely degraded dunes **restoration and repair** of the seaward face by replanting and fencing can be carried out.
3 The cause of the problem can be tackled with holistic solutions.

At Kenfig, South Wales, the sediment supply was reduced by the building of a jetty at Port Talbot. This, combined with sand extraction from the dunes and dredging near shore, reduced the sediment supply to the dunes, leading to a negative sediment budget. A **holistic management** plan (walkways, access permits and keeping out grazing livestock) was the answer.

Strategies to manage the impacts of human activity on coastal processes and landforms

The choice of a suitable case study to illustrate this concept is wide. In this guide new, more sustainable coastal management strategies have been selected, with a detailed study of the Shoreline Management Plan for Barton on Sea, one of the most problematic coastal stretches on the south coast of the UK. An equally relevant approach would be to take a topic such as coastal conflicts caused by human activities and look at a plan to manage them at a small scale, such as issues caused by tourism at the Golfe de Morbihan in Brittany, or issues at Hengistbury Head on the south coast of the UK, or using a fieldwork-based study from the Welsh Coast.

New, more sustainable ways to manage the coast

In the past, coastal management tended to deal with a single issue at a time, for example sediment loss from a particular beach, or collapse from landslip on a cliff face. Each issue was dealt with piecemeal by an individual authority. Although the original issue was often resolved, unintended consequences frequently arose — for example, sediment starvation and subsequently increased erosion downdrift.

Integrated coastal zone management (ICZM) overcomes this piecemeal approach and is now the preferred strategy in most countries of the world, with the development of **holistic management** policies that encompass a wide range of methodologies. It is now recognised that the geographical context of a coastline includes cliffs, beaches, dunes, marshes and estuaries, i.e. the **nearshore** areas *and* river catchments draining into the coast as well as offshore areas. Equally, human impacts on the coast are part of the coastal system. It is important to bring together a wide range of groups and individuals, as there is an increase in the number and variety of stakeholders in the coastal zone.

Increasingly, ICZM has to be integrated **internationally** (i.e. transboundary), for example between nations adjacent to the North Sea or the Mediterranean Sea, because of wider sediment flows. Agenda 21 commits coastal nations to the implementation of integrated coastal zone management initiatives, and to the sustainable development of coastal areas and marine environments under their jurisdiction. With the growing threats of climate warming, and the subsequent accelerating rise in sea level, there is clearly some urgency in the situation.

Sustainable management of the coast is increasingly the primary aim, balancing environmental needs with economic viability and social needs of both coastal and non-coastal dwellers (Table 10). While this is an admirable aim it is often ill-defined, and not easy to achieve in what is a contested environment.

Table 10 The coastal sustainability quadrant

Futurity	Public participation
Using coastal areas for the benefit of the present population, while maintaining their potential for future generations	Ensuring that public stakeholders and individuals have the information and opportunity to take part in the decision-making process about choice of strategy
Environmental and ecofriendly	Equity and social justice
Providing coastal defences that enhance the environment and work with the natural environment	Ensuring that as far as possible the needs of all groups are met when considering options for coastal development, including poor people who have little influence over the decisions

Knowledge check 22

Research the stages in the development of a shoreline management plan (SMP).

Knowledge check 23

Explain why sustainable coastal management is so difficult to achieve.

Case study

One management strategy to manage the impacts of human activity on coastal processes and landforms

Integrated coastal zone management: the shoreline management plan for Barton on Sea

Figure 18 shows the three coastal behavioural units (cliffs in the case of Barton on Sea) for a 6–7 km stretch of the Hampshire coast at Barton on Sea in Christchurch Bay, for which there are three different proposed options resulting from differences in the nature of the coastal zone and the subsequent strategic aims. Table 11 summarises this.

The geology of Christchurch Bay is mainly permeable sedimentary tertiary sands and gravels. At Barton on Sea, the underlying clay is exposed. Mass movement in the form of rotational slumps is caused by these adjacent layers of permeable sands and impermeable clays. Groundwater flows towards the sea from 400 m inland, which increases cliff face erosion and instability.

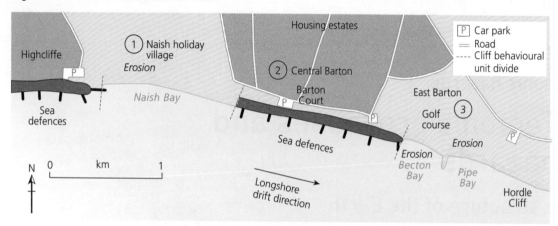

Figure 18 The coast at Barton on Sea

Table 11 Cliff behavioural units and issues

Cliff behavioural units and issues	Management options and decisions
1 West to Naish Farm and Highcliffe Area is a retreating and collapsing cliff, with good exposure of fossiliferous Barton Clay, hence its SSSI conservation status. Active cliff recession escalated from 0.4 m per year in the 1950s to 1.9 m per year in the 1970s, partly from the 'terminal scour' resulting from Highcliffe defences to the west. If no management is carried out, erosion may seriously affect the main Barton defences.	No major sea defences because low value cliff-top use (mobile caravans), and need for fresh fossil exposures and some sediment to feed Barton and Hurst Castle spit downdrift. The SMP-preferred defence option for this zone is 'managed retreat' in the central part of the zone while retaining the rock defences at its eastern and western boundaries at Barton and Highcliffe, respectively. Soft defence techniques, such as shingle recharge, will allow some cliff erosion to continue while keeping the beach front in its present location.
2 Central Barton on Sea Barren, gravelly, defended cliffs, despite being part of SSSI, because of risk to property. An area of previously high erosion rate of →1 m per year now reduced by extensive coastal protection work since the 1930s, but still suffering periodic collapses of parts of the cliffs as in 2001.	The main focus for coastal defences: no new developments at cliff edge (designated a green belt by the New Forest District Council, effectively a type of **red lining** to show on which side planning permission will be given/refused). New or redeveloped properties up to 400 m inland must have special soakaways to reduce groundwater build-up. The SMP's preferred option is to 'hold the existing defence line', justified by a cost–benefit ratio from the loss of economic value of properties inland — but needing major grant aid from Defra to fund a revolutionary inland drainage scheme, from 2007.
3 East of Barton to Becton Bunny Still part of the SSSI, with major retreats in the cliffs but losses only to the golf course.	The SMP option is to '**do nothing**' because of the low value of development inland, with re-routeing of the coastal footpath.

Summary

- Positive impacts of human activity on coastal processes and landforms include management and conservation.
- Protection strategies operate at different scales, including coastal World Heritage Sites at a global scale, marine reserves at a national scale and SSSIs at a local scale.
- Negative impacts of human activity on coastal processes and landforms include offshore dredging and erosion of sand dunes.
- Dredging for aggregate, sand and gravel has adverse impacts on the sea bed, on marine habitats, food webs, birds and mammals. Dredging can lead to a decline in fish stocks

and filter feeders such as mussels. Poisons and nutrients may also be released. The deepening of inshore waters allows larger waves to break close inshore, damaging the coast.
- Sand dunes are important for coastal protection, but they are threatened by changes in vegetation type, urbanisation, development and removal of sand. Tourism and other uses affect 'dune health', as does interference with sediment supply.
- You will need to know a case study of one management strategy to manage the impacts of human activity on coastal processes and landforms.

Tectonic hazards

■Tectonic processes and hazards

The structure of the Earth

The Earth's structure has been analysed by scientists studying patterns of shockwaves (caused by earthquakes). They have identified a number of layers, with different densities, chemical composition and physical properties (see Figure 19).

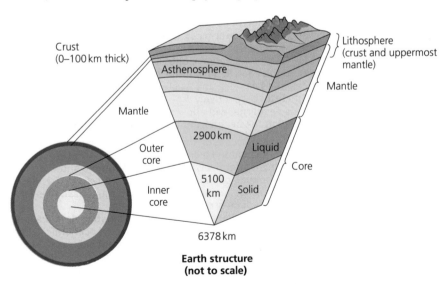

Figure 19 The structure of the Earth

The Earth can be divided into three layers: the core, the mantle and the crust, based on its density and chemical composition.

- The **core** consists of iron and nickel and is about the size of the planet Mars. The outer core is in a semi-molten state but the inner core is solid. The temperature at the centre of the Earth (6378 km below the Earth's surface) is about 6200°C (even hotter than the surface of the sun).

- The **mantle** is composed mainly of silicate rocks, rich in iron and magnesium. Apart from the solid top layer (known as the **asthenosphere**) the rocks in the mantle are in a semi-molten state. The mantle extends to a depth of 2900 km where temperatures may exceed 5000°C. It is this high temperature that generates **convection currents**, which were identified as a mechanism driving plate movements.

- In relative terms, the **crust** is as thin as the skin of an apple is to its flesh. The crust is divided into:

  a **oceanic crust** (known as **sima** as it is composed predominantly of **si**lica and **ma**gnesium), a layer consisting mainly of basalt. It averages 6–10 km in thickness; at its deepest point it has a temperature of 1200°C

  b **continental crust** (**sial**, so called as it is composed of **si**lica and **al**umina), can be up to 70 km thick, and is composed largely of granite

Table 12 summarises the difference between the two types of crust.

Table 12 Differences between the two types of crust

	Oceanic crust	Continental crust
Maximum age	180 million years	3.5 billion years
Thickness (km)	6–10	25–75
Area of Earth's surface	60%	40%
Density (g cm^{-3})	3.3	2.7
Rock type	Basaltic	Granitic

The crust is separated from the mantle by the **Moho discontinuity** (named after Mohorovičić, the Croatian scientist who first discovered it).

The crust and the rigid top layers of the mantle are collectively known as the **lithosphere**.

The mechanics of plate tectonics

The theory of plate tectonics states that the Earth's surface is made up of rigid lithospheric plates (seven major, seven smaller minor, and many more small plates known as micro-plates). There are some areas where the pattern of plate boundaries is so complex, such as Iran and Indonesia, that they appear rather similar to the smashed shells of hard boiled eggs. As can be seen from Figure 20, some plates contain largely continental crust (Eurasian plate), others are composed of continental and oceanic crust, whereas yet others contain only oceanic crust (Nazca plate).

Knowledge check 24

In which layer of the Earth's structure is the asthenosphere found?

Knowledge check 25

Name the seven major plates.

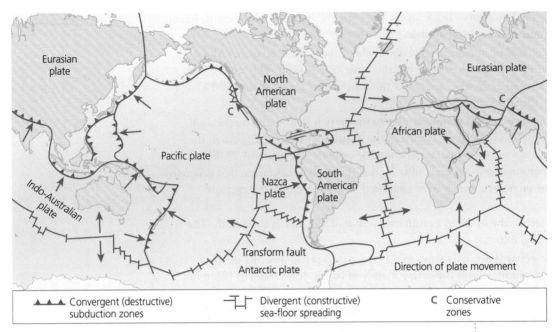

Figure 20 The main tectonic plates

The original idea was that the rising limbs of convection cells (at the spreading ridge) move heat from the Earth's core towards the surface, spreading out either side of the ridge and carrying the plates with it. The plates 'float' on a lubricated layer between the upper mantle and the lithosphere — the asthenosphere. This lubricated layer allows the solid lithosphere to move over the upper mantle (Figure 21).

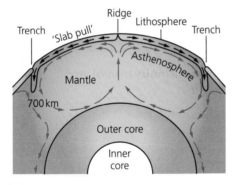

Figure 21 The role of convection currents and slab pull

Modern thinking on plate movement

Modern imaging techniques (tomography) have been unable to identify convection cells in the mantle that are sufficiently large to drive plate movement, so the idea of the asthenosphere as a 'conveyor' of plates has been modified. It has also been discovered that the injection of fresh magma associated with sea floor spreading at the ocean ridges does not **push** the plates apart, instead it is more of a passive process — a case of filling a gap rather than forcibly injecting material into the lithosphere.

Molten material wells up at divergent plate boundaries because of thinning of the lithosphere, and the consequent decrease in pressure causes partial melting of the upper mantle. As the lithosphere is heated, it rises and becomes elevated above the surrounding sea floor to form an ocean ridge. This elevation produces a slope down and away from the ridge. Fresh rock formed at the spreading centres is relatively hot, less dense and more buoyant than rock further away from the divergent margin, which becomes increasingly older, cooler and denser.

Gravity acts on this older, denser lithosphere causing it to slide away from the spreading ridge. As a result, the lithosphere is thinned at the ridge, creating yet more partial melting and upwelling of magma. This process, known as **ridge push**, was initially identified as the key driver of movement but it is now considered to be a passive process — it is the **gravitational sliding** that is now considered to be the active force driving plate movement. It is the density differences across the plates that are of key importance. **Slab pull** occurs at subduction zones where the colder, denser portions of the plates sink into the mantle and this **pulls** the remainder of the plates along. Therefore it is **slab pull** that is the key mechanism for plate movement.

Evidence from tomography (seismic scans) supports this theory as the cold dense slabs of plate deep in the Earth's mantle have been identified.

The development of plate tectonics as a theory evolved over many years from a concept to a credible mechanism, but it remains just a theory because the cost of drilling down for proof is prohibitively expensive and impractical. The mechanism by which tectonic plates move is highly complex and remains a subject of debate.

Exam tip

As plate tectonics is a theory it cannot be proven. Ideas on plate movement mechanisms will develop, so keep up to date. For examples see the USGS website.

Exam tip

When answering questions on plate tectonics do not include the story of continental drift in your answer.

Plate movements

Plates move slowly and irregularly in relation to each other, typically at rates of 4 cm per year. Three types of movement are recognised.

1 In some locations plates move away from each other, i.e. they **diverge** at a **constructive margin**, e.g. East African Rift Valley.
2 In other locations plates move towards each other, i.e. they **converge** at a **destructive** margin, for example off the coast of South America.
3 In a few places plates move past each other, either in opposite directions, or in the same direction at different speeds, i.e. a **transform** movement, at what is called a conservative margin.

Plate tectonic settings

Table 13 summarises the main settings, processes, hazards and landforms. These settings are fundamental in explaining the spatial distribution and occurrence of nearly all tectonic hazards and landforms (see p. 63 for exceptions).

Table 13 Tectonic settings

Tectonic setting	Motion (processes)	Hazards	Example	Landforms
Constructive plate boundaries (divergent margin)	Two oceanic plates moving apart	Basaltic volcanoes and minor, shallow earthquakes	Mid-Atlantic ridge (Iceland), mostly submerged	Lava plateaux Ocean ridge features
	Two continental plates moving apart	Basaltic spatter cones and minor earthquakes	Mt Nyiragongo (DRC) in the East African Rift Valley	Rift valley landscapes
Destructive plate boundaries (convergent margin)	Two oceanic plates in collision	Island arc explosive andesitic eruptions and earthquakes	Soufrière Hills on Montserrat, Aleutian Islands	Island arcs of volcanoes
	Two continental plates in collision	Major, shallow earthquakes, long thrust faults	Himalayan orogenic belt collision zone	Compressional mountain belts
	Oceanic and continental plates in collision	Explosive, andesitic eruptions and major earthquakes	Andes mountain chain and volcanoes	Complex mountain landscapes with fold mountains and volcanoes
Transform boundaries (conservative margin)	Plates sliding past one another	Major shallow earthquakes No volcanic activity	San Andreas fault, California, North Anatolian fault, Haiti	Strike-slip faulted landscapes
Hotspots	Oceanic	Basaltic shield volcanoes and minor earthquakes	Hawaiian island chains, Galapagos Islands	Volcanic landscapes
	Continental	Colossal rhyolitic mega-eruptions	Yellowstone 'supervolcano', USA	'Roots' of super volcanoes

> **Exam tip**
>
> Table 13 is a useful summary. Make sure you learn it.

> **Knowledge check 26**
>
> Which tectonic settings have (a) the most violent earthquakes, (b) the most explosive volcanic eruptions?

Constructive plate margins

Two plates of oceanic crust

The movement of the plates apart is due to the divergence driven by **slab pull**, which brings magma from the asthenosphere to the surface. The pressure from the margins leads to a doming up of the Earth's surface and the formation of a ridge such as the mid-Atlantic ridge (Figure 22). This ridge and rift system extends along the mid Atlantic for about 10,000 km. It was created about 60 million years ago when Greenland (on the North American plate) and northwest Scotland (on the Eurasian plate) separated to form the Atlantic Ocean. The **average** rate of movement is 0.025 m per year. There is a series of underwater volcanoes along the margin, which occasionally form a volcanic island. Iceland is one such volcanic island, much of which formed from a lava plateau about 200 m above sea level, as basic lava poured out through numerous tensional faults (fissures) formed by a hotspot plume. Subsidence of sections of crust between fault lines formed the rift valley, clearly visible at Thingvellir, and there are also active volcanoes such as Hekla and Grimsvotn linked to individual vents from the hotspots.

Most of the earthquake activity at a constructive margin is shallow, low magnitude and high frequency, often along transform faults as the mid-ocean ridge is offset. In June 2000 a significant earthquake, MM scale 6.5, occurred on the south coast of Iceland.

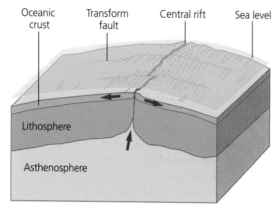

Figure 22 A cross-section of the mid-Atlantic ridge

Two plates of continental crust

The East African Rift Valley is an example of a constructive margin in an area of continental crust. Eastern Africa is moving in a northeasterly direction, diverging from the main African plate, which is 'heading' north. The rift valley, which consists of two broadly parallel branches, extends for 4000 km from Mozambique to the Red Sea. Inward-facing fault line scarps (eroded fault scarps) reach heights more than 600 m above the valley floor.

Knowledge check 27

Explain the difference between a fault scarp and a fault line scarp.

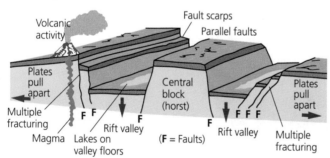

Figure 23 Key features of the rift valley landscape

Figure 23 shows the following features.
- Linear mountain ranges (ridges) form as a result of the buoyancy of hot, low-density margins, which forces the crust to bulge upwards along the plate margins.
- A central rift in the ridge forms because of subsidence between normal faults to form a rift valley.
- Chains of lakes (e.g. Lake Tanganyika) form in the basins as the rift opens up.
- Fissure eruptions occur from a series of basaltic lava flows.

- Some large volcanoes (e.g. Kilimanjaro) form where the crust has thinned by tension and rising magma is extruded through the weaknesses.
- Numerous small basaltic cinder cones form on the rift valley floor, often made of lava and some ash (composite).
- Minor igneous intrusions occur, flowing up through the faults and fissures to form dykes.

Over time the rift valley is reshaped, for example by waterfalls cascading over the lava plateau and by present-day weathering and mass movement on the fault scarp to create fault line scarps.

Destructive plate margins

Destructive plate margins occur when two plates converge due to slab pull.

Ocean crust to ocean crust

When two oceanic plates converge, subduction occurs, as one plate is likely to be slightly older, colder or denser than the other. This plate is **subducted**, heated and eventually melts under pressure at around 100 km below the surface. The melted material rises up through any lines of weakness towards the surface. Extrusive volcanic activity results in the formation of a chain of volcanic islands above the subduction zone, known as **an island arc**. As Figure 24 shows, the Mariana Islands have been formed in this way through the convergence of the Pacific plate and the Philippine plate, with the Pacific plate being subducted to form the deep Marianas Trench. Earthquakes of high magnitude are focused along the subducted plate (the **Benioff zone**).

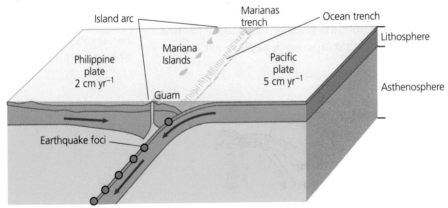

Figure 24 Cross-section of an oceanic/oceanic destructive margin

Oceanic to continental

Oceanic crust is denser than continental crust, so where these two types of crust converge, the more dense crust is subducted down into the asthenosphere by slab pull. Again, an ocean trench is formed on the sea floor at the point of **subduction**. The continental crust, because it is lighter and more buoyant, is not subducted but is uplifted and buckled, faulted and folded to form a range of mountains (Figure 25). Rising magma again breaks through any lines of weakness to form volcanoes, with infrequent but violent eruptions, or may solidify beneath the surface, forming intrusive igneous rocks such as granite batholiths which can be subsequently exposed by numerous years of erosion.

An example is found in South America, where the oceanic Nazca plate is moving east at approximately 12 cm per year and is converging with and subducting beneath the continental South American plate, which is moving west at 1 cm per year. The Andes, a chain of fold mountains, rises nearly 7000 m above sea level, interspersed with many active volcanoes such as Cotopaxi in Ecuador. The Peru–Chile trench, which reaches depths of 8000 m, occurs at the point of subduction. Earthquakes (e.g. in northern Peru in 1970 and in Ecuador in 2016) are frequent and often of huge magnitude (up to MM 9) and occur at a range of depths along the Benioff zone.

> **Exam tip**
>
> Learn diagrams of all the major types of plate movement. Use full annotations.

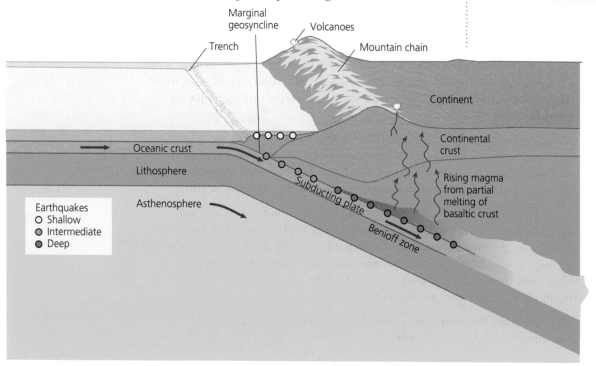

Figure 25 Cross-section of oceanic/continental destructive margin

Continental to continental: collision margins

Where two plates of continental crust converge is known as a **collision margin**. As the plates are both buoyant and composed of lower density granite material, no subduction occurs. However, former ocean sediments trapped between the two converging plates are heaved upward, under intense compression (formation of **thrust faults** and nappes), resulting in the formation of major complex mountain belts. Usually no volcanic activity is found at this type of margin as no crust is being destroyed by subduction and no new crust is being created by rising magma. However, earthquakes do occur. Some are of deeper focus and therefore have less surface impact, but shallow, highly hazardous earthquakes also occur, often in populated foothill areas as in Nepal.

A good example of a collision zone is the Himalayas. The Indo-Australian plate is moving northwards at a rate of about 5–6 cm per year, so colliding with the Eurasian plate. Prior to their collision, the two continental landmasses were separated by the remnants of the Tethys Sea, which originated when Pangaea broke up around 300 million years ago.

As the two plates collided, the Himalayas were formed (orogenesis). These mountain belts are geologically complex as the intense compression caused not only extreme folds (nappes), but also thrust faults and accretionary wedging on uplift. The mountain belt rises to heights of 9000 m and includes Mt Everest. The huge thickness of sediment forced the crust downwards (isostatic depression) and the roots of the mountain belt are found deep in the Earth's interior. The collision movement causes great stresses which are released by periodic earthquakes, such as the Gorkha earthquake in Nepal, 2015.

Knowledge check 28

Define the term 'orogenesis'.

Conservative plate margins

A conservative margin is found where two plates move laterally past each other — this is known as a **transform movement**. As at collision margins there is no volcanic activity here because no crust is being destroyed by subduction and no new crust is being created by rising magma. However, shallow earthquakes of varying frequency and magnitude do occur.

High frequency, low magnitude earthquakes occur when pressure along the margin is relatively easily released, usually up to ten every day. Occasional major events take place after a significant build-up of pressure, typically when high levels of friction restrict movement along the original fault lines (e.g. the Haiti earthquake of 2010).

The best-known example of a conservative margin occurs in California at the San Andreas fault, where the Pacific plate and North American plate meet. The Pacific plate is moving northwestwards at a rate of 6 cm per year, while the North American plate, although moving in the same general direction, is only moving at about 1 cm per year. While earth tremors are very common, the 'Big One', such as occurred at San Francisco in 1906 and 1989, occurs only rarely.

Figure 26 summarises the main features found at a conservative margin, largely associated with erosion along the fault line.

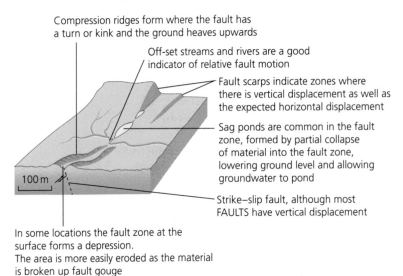

Figure 26 The main features of a conservative margin

Hotspots

Hotspots are small areas of the crust with an unusually high heat flow and are found away from plate boundaries.

Oceanic hotspots occur where plumes of magma are rising from the asthenosphere. If the crust is particularly thin or weak, magma may escape onto the surface as a volcanic eruption. Lava may build up over time until it is above the present-day sea level, giving rise to volcanic islands.

The Hawaiian islands are a chain of volcanic islands (Figure 27) lying over a stable hotspot. The Pacific plate has been moving over the hotspot for about 70 million years, forming a succession of volcanic islands. As the plate has moved, so the volcanoes have been carried away from the hotspot in a northwesterly direction, forming a chain of extinct underwater volcanoes, called **sea mounts**, extending all the way towards the Aleutian Islands. Currently a new volcano, called Loihi, is erupting 35 km southeast of Big Island (Hawaii). It is only 3000 m tall and has risen only to 2000 m below sea level to date — it is estimated to reach the sea surface in 10,000–100,000 years' time. Big Island (Hawaii) volcanoes are extremely active — with frequent effusive eruptions from Kilauea. The high peaks Mauna Kea and Mauna Loa are actually higher than Mt Everest, but they start from well below sea level.

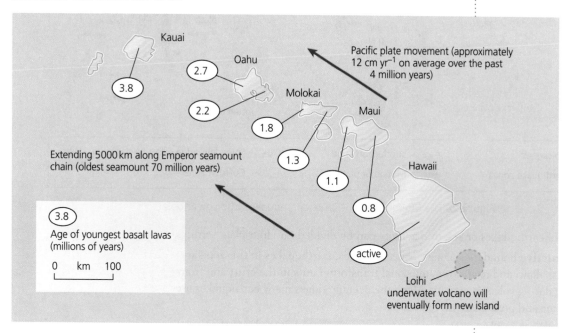

Figure 27 The Hawaiian hotspot

An example of a **continental hotspot** is found beneath Yellowstone National Park. The key feature is the probable explosive eruption of a rhyolitic super volcano, at the maximum of the VEI scale (see pp. 66–67). Geological records suggest the Yellowstone event occurred 2.1 million years ago, ejecting 6000 times more gas and molten rock into the atmosphere than did the Mt St Helens eruption.

Global distribution of tectonic hazards

Primary tectonic hazards include earthquakes and volcanoes.

Exam tip

Re-read Table 13
Tectonic settings on p. 56
to piece together the key
facts regarding the
distribution of earthquakes
and volcanoes,
summarised here.

Earthquakes

Figure 28 shows the distribution of 30,000 earthquakes recorded over the last decade. The figure shows that the main zones of earthquakes are *not* randomly distributed but closely follow the plate boundaries.

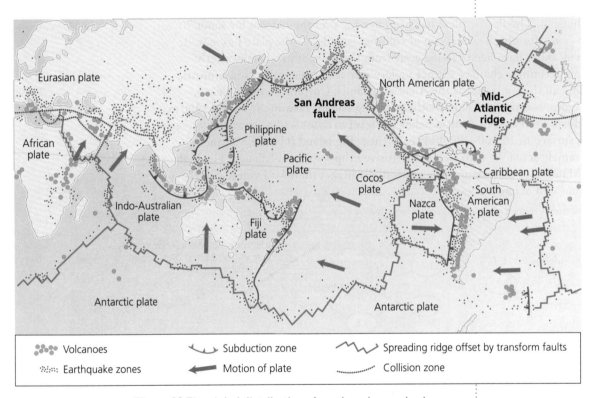

Figure 28 The global distribution of earthquakes and volcanoes

The zones of earthquakes or **seismic** activity can be divided into four plate settings.

1 **Constructive** boundaries along the ocean ridges. Earthquakes in this zone are mainly shallow, and result from tensional transform faults in the crust and from shaking during volcanic activity. Along the oceanic ridges many earthquakes are submarine and pose little risk to people.

2 **Destructive** boundaries where oceanic crust is being subducted into the mantle beneath a continental plate, or where two oceanic plates collide in island arc zones. These areas are subject to frequent earthquakes, including high magnitude ones, and represent areas of major hazard. Tsunamis are most commonly generated by these earthquakes (e.g. 2004 Boxing Day tsunami).

3 **Destructive** boundaries where continental crust is colliding to produce fold mountain belts, e.g. the Alpine–Himalayan chain. Shallow earthquakes occur in a relatively broad zone, resulting in a high hazard risk (e.g. 1990 Bam earthquake in Iran) with the occasional deep-seated earthquake.

4   Areas of lateral crust movement (**transform**) in the continental regions produce mainly shallow earthquakes of high magnitude, such as at the conservative margin of the San Andreas fault system in California.

Additionally **intra-plate** earthquakes occur — some 15% of all earthquakes occur in relatively stable continental crust, away from plate boundaries. These earthquakes are caused by stresses created in crustal rocks, usually by movement along ancient fault lines (e.g. New Madrid in Missouri, USA, 1811/1812 and Tangshen in China, 1976, which resulted in 240,000 deaths), a process known as **isostatic recoil**. These intra-plate earthquakes are more dangerous because they are extremely unpredictable.

Quasi-natural earthquakes are those generated by human activity. It is thought that a 1993 earthquake in Killari, India, possibly resulted from the weight of water in a newly built reservoir behind a dam causing increased water pressure in the rock pores, which lubricated a fault line.

A recent controversial generator of earthquakes is **fracking** for unconventional supplies of oil and gas, which has led to numerous earthquakes in Oklahoma, and also in north Lancashire in the UK where fracking exploration was halted in 2015 as a result.

Volcanoes

The chemical composition of lava depends on the geological situation in which it has formed. Basaltic (basic) lavas are formed by the melting of oceanic crust, whereas rhyolitic (acidic) lavas with a high silica content are formed from the melting of continental crust. Between these extremes are several groups of intermediate magmas, such as andesitic magma.

The world's active volcanoes are found in three tectonic situations (see Figure 28).

1   **Constructive plate boundaries (rift volcanoes).** Most of the magma that reaches the Earth's surface (around 75% in quantity) is extruded along these boundaries. This mainly occurs at **mid-ocean ridges** where melting of the upper mantle produces basaltic magma. The eruptions tend to be non-violent (VEI 1–2, see p. 67) and, as most occur on the sea floor, they do not represent a major hazard to people except where portions of the ocean ridge cross inhabited islands, such as Iceland. Fissure eruptions producing lava plateaux also occur widely. **Continental** constructive boundaries, such as the East African Rift Valley system, also have active volcanoes with a wide range of magma types depending on the local geological conditions through which the magma passes before reaching the surface.

2   **Destructive plate boundaries (subduction volcanoes).** Some 80% of the world's active volcanoes occur along destructive boundaries. As the oceanic plate is subducted into the mantle and melts under pressure, basic magma rises upwards and mixes with the continental crust to produce largely intermediate magma with a higher silica content than at the ocean ridges. These andesitic, in some cases more acidic, rhyolitic magmas can cause violent volcanic activity.

3   **Hotspots.** See p. 61. Examples of active hotspots include the Hawaiian Islands, Iceland, the Galapagos and the Azores. Eruptions are usually effusive with huge quantities of low viscosity basaltic magmas, and are therefore less hazardous for people even in populated areas, although they can cause considerable damage to infrastructure and property.

Exam tip

Always support your arguments with brief locational fact files of examples.

Knowledge check 29

Explain why fracking can lead to earthquakes.

Knowledge check 30

Explain the difference between magma and lava.

Physical hazard profiles and their impacts

Figure 29 compares the three major tectonic hazards in terms of their physical profiles. This is a qualitative technique that can be used to visually compare major hazard types, but also to look at a range of earthquakes or a series of volcanic eruptions.

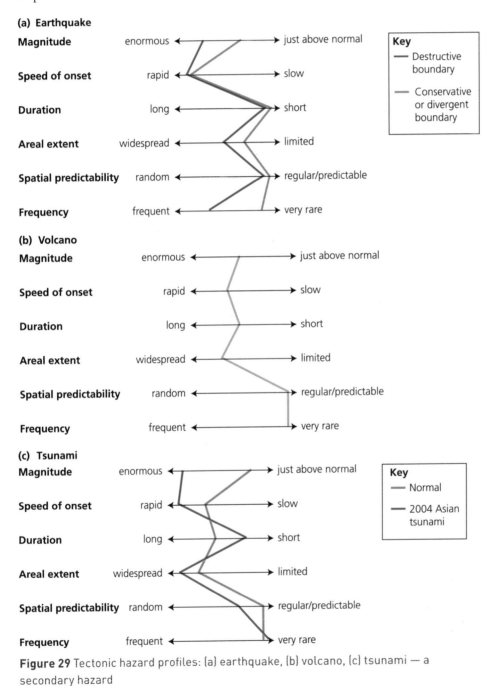

Figure 29 Tectonic hazard profiles: (a) earthquake, (b) volcano, (c) tsunami — a secondary hazard

Magnitude of earthquakes

Magnitude is considered to be the most important influence on the severity of impact of a tectonic hazard event. Magnitude is a quantifiable variable, especially for earthquakes. It can be defined as the size or physical force of a hazard event.

Earthquake magnitude is now measured by the logarithmic Moment Magnitude (MM) scale, a modification of the earlier **Richter scale**. The Richter scale was based on the amplitude of lines made on a seismogram, using the largest wave amplitude recorded. So the bigger the earthquake, the greater the earth shaking. For example, a 1-unit increase on the scale represents a ten times larger amplitude, i.e. it is a **logarithmic scale**. The MM scale is based on a number of parameters of an earthquake event, including the area of fault rupture and the amount of fault movement involved, which determines the amount of energy released. Results are similar to the Richter scale which is still widely used.

The **Mercalli scale** is also used to measure earthquakes. It is a descriptive scale that measures the amount of damage caused by surface shaking of particular earthquakes (see Table 14). Table 15 shows the relationship between earthquake magnitude and number of deaths resulting in a sample decade.

> **Exam tip**
>
> Use the MM scale, now widely used, as it is an improved version of the Richter scale.

> **Exam tip**
>
> Try to learn simple tables of dates, locations, magnitude and impacts of tectonic events.

Table 14 Abridged modified Mercalli intensity scale

Average peak velocity (cm s⁻¹)	Intensity value and description
1–2	**I** Not felt, except by a very few under exceptionally favourable circumstances **II** Felt only by a few persons at rest, especially on upper floors of buildings. Delicately suspended objects may swing
2–5	**III** Felt quite noticeably indoors, especially on upper floors of buildings, but many people do not recognise it as an earthquake. Standing automobiles may rock slightly. Vibration like passing truck. Duration estimated
5–8	**IV** During day felt indoors by many, outdoors by few. At night some awakened. Dishes, windows, doors disturbed; walls make creaking sound. Sensation like heavy truck striking building. Standing automobiles rocked noticeably
8–12	**V** Felt by nearly everyone, many awakened. Some dishes, windows etc. broken; cracked plaster in a few places; unstable objects overturned. Disturbance of trees, poles and other tall objects sometimes noticed. Pendulum clocks may stop
20–30	**VI** Felt by all, many frightened and run outdoors. Some heavy furniture moved; a few instances of fallen plaster and damaged chimneys. Damage slight **VII** Everybody runs outdoors. Damage negligible in buildings of good design and construction; slight to moderate in well-built ordinary structure; considerable in poorly built or badly designed structures; some chimneys broken. Noticed by persons driving cars
45–55	**VIII** Damage slight in specially designed structures; considerable in ordinary substantial buildings, with partial collapse; great in poorly built structures. Panel walls thrown out of frame structure. Fall of chimneys, factory stacks, columns, walls, monuments. Heavy furniture overturned. Sand and mud ejected in small amounts. Changes in well water. Persons driving cars disturbed
> 60	**IX** Damage considerable in specially designed structures; well-designed frame structures thrown out of plumb; damage great in substantial buildings, with partial collapse. Buildings shifted off foundations. Ground cracked conspicuously. Underground pipes broken **X** Some well-built wooden structures destroyed; most masonry and frame structures destroyed including foundations; ground badly cracked. Rails bent. Landslides considerable from river banks and steep slopes. Shifted sand and mud. Water splashed, slopped over banks **XI** Few, if any (masonry) structures remain standing. Bridges destroyed. Broad fissures in ground. Underground pipelines completely out of surface. Earth slumps and landslips in soft ground. Rails bend greatly **XII** Damage total. Waves seen on ground surface. Lines of sight and level distorted. Objects thrown into the air

Table 15 The relationship between earthquake magnitude and number of deaths resulting

Date	Region	Magnitude	Deaths
2011, March 11	East coast of Honshu, Japan	9.0	28,050
2010, January 12	Port-au-Prince, Haiti	7.0	220,000
2009, September 30	Southern Sumatra, Indonesia	7.5	1,117
2008, May 12	Eastern Sichuan, China	7.9	87,587
2006, May 26	Java, Indonesia	6.3	5,749
2005, October 8	Kashmir, E Pakistan/northwest India	7.6	73,000
2004, December 26	Sumatra and Indian Ocean	9.1	227,898
2003, December 26	Bam, southeast Iran	6.6	30,000
2002, March 25	Hindu Kush, Afghanistan	6.1	1,000
2001, January 21	Gujarat, northwest India	7.9	20,023

Magnitude of volcanic eruptions

All volcanoes are formed from molten material (magma) in the Earth's crust. There is no fully agreed scale for measuring the size of eruptions, but Newhall and Self (1982) drew up a semi-quantitative **volcanic explosivity index** (**VEI**), which can be related to the type of magma that influences the type of eruption. It combined:

■ the total volume of ejected products
■ the height of the eruption cloud
■ the duration of the main eruptive phase
■ several other items such as eruption rate

into a basic 0–8 scale of increasing hazard. The results can be related to the type of volcanic eruption.

For example, the 1991 eruption of Mt Pinatubo in the Philippines was a **Plinian type** of eruption with a plume of tephra ejected more than 30 km into the atmosphere and was classified as a VEI 5–6. The VEI is, despite all the measurements, only a partly quantitative scale and it has several important limitations. For example, all types of ejected material are treated alike, and no account is taken of SO_2 emissions, which are needed to quantify the impact of eruptions on climate change. Most of the very large eruptions (VEI 6–8) happened in geological time. Measuring the scale of volcanic eruptions is challenging as there are so many different types. Table 16 shows how volcanic eruptions can be classified using the VEI.

Note that the VEI is a logarithmic scale, because each step of the scale represents a ten-fold increase in material ejected.

Magnitude is largely measureable (easier for earthquakes) and can clearly influence impact.

Table 16 The volcanic explosion index (VEI) scale

Volcanic explosivity index (VEI)	Eruption rate (kg s^{-1})	Volume of ejecta (m^3)	Eruption column height (km)	Duration of continuous blasts (h)	Troposphere/ stratosphere injection	Qualitative description	Example
0 Non-explosive	10^2–10^3	<10^4	0.8–1.5	<1	Negligible/ none	Effusive	Kilauea, erupts continuously
1 Small	10^3–10^4	10^4–10^6	1.5–2.8	<1	Minor/none	Gentle	Nyiragongo, 2002
2 Moderate	10^4–10^5	10^6–10^7	2.8–5.5	1–6	Moderate/ none	Explosive	Galeras, Columbia, 1993
3 Moderate–large	10^5–10^6	10^7–10^8	5.5–10.5	1–12	Great/possible	Severe	Nevada del Ruiz, 1985
4 Large	10^6–10^7	10^8–10^9	10.5–17.0	1–>12	Great/definite	Violent	Mayon, 1895 Eyjafjallajökull, 2010
5 Very large	10^7–10^8	10^9–10^{10}	17.0–28.0	6–>12	Great/ significant	Cataclysmic	Vesuvius, AD79 Mt St Helens, 1980
6 Very large	10^8–10^9	10^{10}–10^{11}	28.0–47.0	>12	Great/ significant	Paroxysmal	Mt Pinatubo, 1991
7 Very large	>10^9	10^{11}–10^{12}	>47.0	>12	Great/ significant	Colossal	Tambora, 1815
8 Very large	–	>10^{12}	–	>12	Great/ significant	Terrific	Yellowstone, millions of years ago

Frequency

Frequency (i.e. how often an event occurs) is sometimes called the **recurrence** level, e.g. for a 1 in 100 year event. There is an inverse relationship between frequency and magnitude, i.e. the larger the magnitude of the event, the less frequent its occurrence. The effect of frequency on severity of impact is difficult to gauge. Theoretically, areas that experience frequent tectonic events have both adaptation and mitigation measures in place, including extensive monitoring (useful for volcanoes), education and community awareness about what to do (useful for earthquakes or tsunami evacuation routes), and various technological strategies for shockproof building design (Tokyo, San Francisco) or protection (Japanese tsunami walls). It is well known that unexpected tectonic events, such as the 1993 Killari earthquake, can be particularly devastating. On the other hand, familiarity with a frequently erupting volcano, such as Mt Merapi in Indonesia, can breed contempt, as local people are so used to its eruptions that they do not always evacuate soon enough.

Duration

Duration is the length of time for which the tectonic hazard exists. Often an initial earthquake event is followed by massive aftershocks (e.g. Christchurch 2010 and central Italy, 2014) or a series of eruptions occurs. While individual earthquakes often last for only around 30 seconds, the damage can be extensive.

Knowledge check 31

Define the term 'aftershock' and explain its significance for the Christchurch earthquakes.

Secondary hazards often prolong the duration of impact and increase the damage, for example the Tohoku multi-disaster (earthquake, tsunami and nuclear accident). Secondary hazards associated with volcanic eruptions include **lahars** (e.g. Mt Pinatubo; see p. 74) or **jökulhlaup** (glacier bursts) (see p. 74), which are very damaging because of their spatial and temporal unpredictability. In November 1985, the melting of the ice cap and snow on Nevada del Ruiz volcano (p. 76) released huge mudflows that overwhelmed Armero and the surrounding villages, killing 23,000 people. Locally, Himalayan earthquakes such as Kashmir 2005 and Sichuan 2008, cause widespread landslides that disrupt rescue and recovery and add to the death toll.

Areal extent

Areal extent is the size of the area covered by the tectonic hazard and this has a clear impact (see Figure 30).

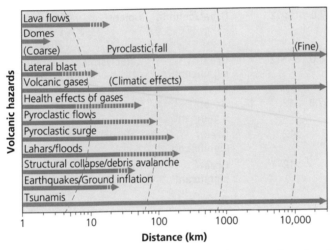

Figure 30 The areal extent of the impacts of various features of a volcanic eruption

Spatial concentration

Spatial concentration is the areal distribution of tectonic hazards over geographical space. It is controlled largely by type of plate boundary. In theory, permanent settlement is avoided in hazardous regions but often such locations present other opportunities, for example some volcanic soils are very fertile, so agricultural settlement occurs, such as on the flanks of Mt Merapi, Indonesia. Equally spring water may be available, such as at Bam, the site of a severe earthquake. Active tectonic, especially volcanic, landscapes encourage tourism, as was seen in the recent unexpected Japanese eruption (Ontaki), where many of the 48 dead were hikers.

Speed of onset

Speed of onset can be a crucial factor. Earthquakes generally come with little warning. The speed of onset and the almost immediate shaking of the ground led to maximum destruction by the Kobe earthquake, but this was allied with other factors such as timing and building type. The 2004 Boxing Day tsunami illustrates the variation well (see p. 101) with little awareness of the hazard possible at Aceh, Indonesia, but, theoretically, warnings and therefore evacuation were possible everywhere else.

This was in spite of a lack of a sophisticated warning system (subsequently built) for the Indian Ocean, unlike that which existed in the Pacific Ocean, based on Hawaii.

Predictability of occurrence

The random temporal distribution of both earthquakes and volcanoes can add to their potential impact. While **gap theory** can increase the possibility of predicting the 'Big One', in reality earthquakes are unpredictable. Volcanic eruptions can also be hard to predict precisely, even with close monitoring, hence discussions concerning the possible and long-awaited eruption of Vesuvius in the densely settled Bay of Naples.

Knowledge check 32

Explain seismic gap theory and its role in earthquake prediction.

Summary

- The Earth's structure has a number of layers: the inner core, outer core, mantle and crust, each with different densities, chemical composition and physical properties.
- The theory of plate tectonics states that the Earth's surface is made up of rigid plates, 'floating' on the asthenosphere. It was thought that their movement was powered by convection currents from radioactive decay in the Earth's core, but today it is thought that gravitational sliding is the force driving plate movement and slab pull is the key mechanism.
- Plates move in three ways: diverging at a constructive margin, converging at a destructive margin, or making a transform movement at a conservative margin. These movements occur under the oceans and on the continents with different results.
- Hotspots are small areas of the crust with an unusually high heat flow, away from plate boundaries.
- The main zones of earthquakes closely follow the plate boundaries but intra-plate earthquakes and quasi-natural earthquakes generated by human activity, also occur.
- Active volcanoes are found along constructive plate boundaries, destructive plate boundaries and at hotspots.
- The characteristics of the physical hazard profile that influence its impact include magnitude (Mercalli and Richter scales and volcanic explosivity index), predictability, frequency, duration, speed of onset and areal extent.

Volcanoes, processes, hazards and their impacts

Types of volcanoes

Volcanoes can be classified by their **shape** and the nature of the **vent** the magma is extruded through, as well as the nature of the **eruption**.

Shape of the volcano and its vent

Figure 31 shows how volcanoes can be classified by shape. The shape is, of course, largely dependent on the material erupted, which itself can be linked back to the tectonic setting.
- **Fissure eruptions** result when lava is ejected through tensional linear fissures, rather than a central vent, at divergent plate boundaries. The Haimeay eruption in Iceland of 1973 began with a fissure 2 km long, through which lava poured effusively.

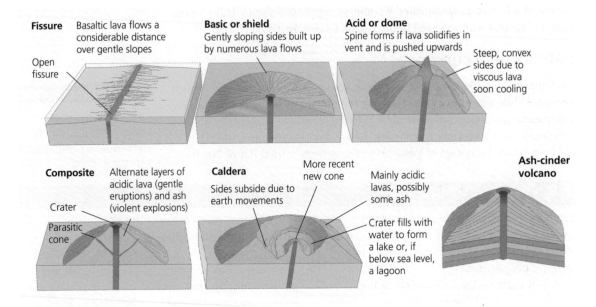

Figure 31 Types of volcano by shape

- **Shield volcanoes**, such as Mauna Kea in Hawaii, are formed when basaltic lava pours in huge quantities out of a central vent. Because of the effusive nature of the basic fluid lava, it can spread over a wide area before solidifying. The result is a huge volcanic cone but with gently sloping sides. The lava has low viscosity because of its low (<50%) silica content, and erupts at temperatures of about 1200°C. Mauna Loa in Hawaii has built up a cone that rises 9000 m from the sea floor, with a diameter of 120 km at its base, sloping at about 6° to the top. Shield volcanoes occur at both oceanic diverging plates and hotspots.

- **Composite cones or strato-volcanoes** form from alternating layers of lava and ash, resulting from eruptions at destructive plate margins. The lava itself is typically acidic with more than 50% silica content. It has a temperature of about 800°C. This means it flows more slowly, creating cones with more steeply sloping sides. The ash is produced in a highly explosive eruptive phase, often after the vent has been blocked. Many of the world's well known volcanoes, such as Mt Etna, Vesuvius and Popocatepetl, are composite volcanoes. Etna is a classic cone shape with slopes of 50° near its base, but slopes of only 30° at the summit, with a marked crater.

- **Acid or dome volcanoes** result when acid lava quickly solidifies on exposure to the air. These volcanoes frequently have parasitic cones formed as the passage of the rising rhyolitic magma through the main vent is blocked. The cones are steep sided and convex in shape. In one extreme example (Mt Pelée) the lava actually solidified as it came up the vent, producing a spine, rather than flowing down the sides.

- **Ash and cinder cones** such as Paricutin are formed when ash and cinders build up in a cylindrical cone of relatively small size. They are highly permeable as they are composed of loose volcanic cinders. A typical size is 800 m in height, with a bowl-shaped crater.

■ **Calderas** occur when the build-up of gases becomes extreme. Huge explosions may clear the magma chamber beneath the volcano and remove the summit of the cone, or cauldron subsidence may occur. This causes the sides of the crater to collapse and subside, thus widening the opening to several kilometres in diameter. Frequently, enlarged craters or calderas have been flooded and later eruptions have formed smaller cones in the resulting lake, e.g. Wizard Island in Crater Lake Oregon.

Nature of the eruption

The nature of the eruption is also significant. Table 17 summarises the major categories of eruption, based on the degree of violence/explosivity, a consequence of pressure and the amount of gas in the magma.

Table 17 Major categories of eruption

	Category	Description
Effusive	Icelandic	Lava flows directly from a fissure
	Hawaiian	Lava is emitted gently from a vent
	Strombolian	Small but frequent eruptions occur
	Vulcanian	More violent and less frequent
	Vesuvian	Violent explosion after a long period of inactivity
	Krakatoan	Exceptionally violent explosion
	Pelean	Violent eruption of pyroclastic flows (nuées ardentes)
Explosive	Plinian	Large amounts of lava and pyroclastic material are ejected

Volcanic processes and the production of associated hazards

Pyroclastic flows and surges

Pyroclastic flows have been responsible for most volcanic deaths to date. They are sometimes called **nuées ardentes** ('glowing clouds') and result from frothing of the molten magma in the volcano vent. Bubbles in the magma burst explosively to eject a lethal mixture of hot gases and pyroclastic material (volcanic fragments, ash, pumice and glass shapes). Pyroclastic bursts surge downhill because, as they contain a heavy load of rock fragment and dust, they are denser than the surrounding air. The clouds may be literally red hot (up to 1000°C). The greatest risks occur when the summit crater is blocked by viscous rhyolitic magma and blasts are directed laterally in Peléan type eruptions, in surges of $30\,\mathrm{m\,s^{-1}}$, close to the ground and up to 30–40 km from the source.

There is little warning of these events; people exposed are killed immediately by severe external and internal burns combined with asphyxiation. The cloud which hit the town of St Pierre, Martinique (6 km from the centre of the VEI 6 eruption) in the Mont Pelée disaster of 1902 had a temperature of 700°C and travelled at $33\,\mathrm{m\,s^{-1}}$ down the River Blanche Valley. All but three of the inhabitants of St Pierre (around 30,000 in all) were killed. One was saved by being in the jail!

Lava flows

While lava flows are spectacular, they pose more threat to property than human life (e.g. eruptions of Kilauea, the destruction of much of the village of Kapilani, covering $78\,km^2$ and destroying nearly 200 houses). The lava flows most dangerous to human life come from fissure eruptions, not central vents, as highly fluid basalt magma can move down a hillside at $50\,km\,h^{-1}$ and can spread a long way from the source. One deadly lava flow erupted from Nyiragongo volcano's flanks, draining the lava lake which had collected at the summit; it killed 72 people and devastated the town of Goma in the Democratic Republic of the Congo.

Pahoehoe lava is the most liquid of all lava, and tends to form a ropey wrinkled surface. On steep slopes this low viscosity lava can move downhill at speeds approaching $15\,m\,s^{-1}$.

A'a lava tends to form blocks, and moves more slowly downhill, leaving a rough irregular surface.

The greatest lava-related disaster in historic times occurred in 1783 when huge quantities of lava poured out of the $24\,km$ long Laki fissure in Iceland. Although there were few direct deaths the resultant famines from lack of crop growth killed more than 10,000 people, around 20% of Iceland's population.

Airfall tephra (ash falls)

Tephra consists of all the fragmented material ejected by the volcano which subsequently falls to the ground. The large explosive eruptions of Mt St Helens (VEI 5) produced an estimated $6\,km^3$ volume of material, which covered a wide area of northwest USA. The particles ranged in size from so-called 'bombs' (>32 m in diameter) down to fine ash and dust (<4 mm in diameter). Coarser, heavier particles fall out of the sky close to the volcano vent. Occasionally tephra is sufficiently hot to spontaneously combust and start fires. Ash clouds can be blown many miles away from the original eruption by strong winds.

Large eruptions such as Krakatoa (VEI 6) in 1883, which spread an aerosol cloud around the globe within 2 weeks, and Tambora, Indonesia 1816 (VEI 7), which led to short-term global cooling of around 1–2 years, could be prolonged to a decadal scale by successive eruptions.

Although ash falls account for fewer than 5% of direct deaths associated with volcanic eruptions (usually respiratory problems), they can create a number of problems.

- Heavy falls of cinders and ash can blanket the landscape, contaminating farmland and poisoning livestock.
- Ash causes health issues such as skin abrasion and breathing problems (silicosis, chronic obstructive pulmonary disease (COPD)).
- The weight of ash can damage roofs.
- Ash washes into lakes and rivers to become a lahar source.
- Wet ash conducts electricity and can cause failure of electronic equipment.
- Fine ash can clog air filters and damage vehicles and aero engines.
- Ash can lead to vehicle accidents, poor visibility, slippery roads.

Exam tip

Research the 2010 Eyjafjallajökull eruption, which had a huge impact on the world economy because it brought flights to a standstill, with enormous global impacts. It is a unique case study.

Volcanic gases

Large amounts and a wide range of gases are released from explosive eruptions and from cooling lava. The complex gas mixture includes water vapour, hydrogen, carbon monoxide, carbon dioxide, hydrogen sulphate, sulphur dioxide, chlorine and hydrogen chloride in variable amounts.

Carbon monoxide causes deaths because of its toxic effects at very low concentrations, but most fatalities have been associated with carbon dioxide (CO_2) releases, because CO_2 is colourless and odourless. In Indonesia, as villagers were evacuating following the eruption of Mt Merapi, they walked into a dense pool of volcanically released CO_2 which had sunk (it is denser than air); 140 were asphyxiated.

The release of CO_2 from past volcanic activity can also create a highly unusual threat. In 1984 a cloud of gas, rich in CO_2, burst out of the volcanic crater of Lake Monoun, Cameroon, killing 37 people. Two years later in 1986, a similar disaster occurred at Lake Nyos crater, Cameroon, killing 1746 people and more than 8000 livestock. The outburst of gas created a fountain that reached 100 m above the lake, before the dense cloud flowed down two valleys to cover an area of more than 60 km².

These rare hazards are the result of unusually high levels of CO_2 in the volcanic lakes. The levels probably build up over a long period of time from CO_2-rich groundwater springs flowing into the submerged craters.

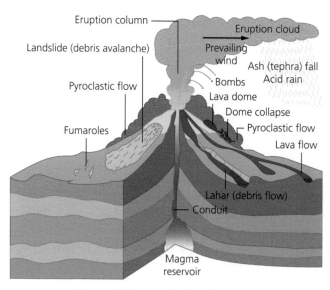

Figure 32 Types of volcanic hazard

Knowledge check 33

Using examples, distinguish between primary, secondary and tertiary tectonic hazards.

Secondary volcanic hazards

Lahars

After pyroclastic flows, lahars present the greatest risk to human life. They can be defined as volcanic mudflows composed of largely silt-size sediments. Lahars consist of volcanic ash and rock up to at least 40% by weight, combined with the torrential rain which often accompanies volcanic eruptions. They create dense, viscous flows that can travel even faster than clear-water streams. They occur widely on steep volcanic flanks, especially in tropical humid or monsoon climates (*lahar* is an Indonesian term).

The degree of hazard varies greatly but generally the flows that contain the larger size sediments are the more deadly. At Mt Pinatubo in the Philippines, lahars regularly transport and deposit tens of millions of cubic metres of sediment in a day and are a potential threat to the local population of over 100,000 people.

Lahars can be classified as **primary**, occurring directly during a volcanic eruption (usually **hot flows**), and **secondary**, which are triggered by high intensity rainfall between eruptions which reactivate old flows of ash etc.

Some lahars are generated by rapid melting of snow and ice — a particular hazard in northern Andean volcanoes. The second deadliest disaster in recent times was caused by the eruption of Nevada del Ruiz volcano (see p. 76).

Volcanic landslides

Landslides and debris avalanches are a common feature of volcano-related ground failure. They are particularly associated with eruptions of siliceous acidic dacitic magma of relatively high viscosity with a large content of dissolved gas.

Volcanic landslides are gravity-driven slides of masses of rock and loose volcanic material. They can occur during an eruption, such as Mt St Helens when the side of the volcano collapsed to form massive landslides and debris avalanches containing $2.7\,km^3$ of material. They can be set off as a result of heavy rainfall or, more commonly, earthquakes.

Ground deformation of volcanic slopes by rising magma, which creates a bulge, can also trigger slope instability and landslides before an eruption, e.g. prior to the Mt St Helens events. Swarms of small earthquakes there were followed by ground uplift and the formation of a huge bulge prior to the main eruption, and then the final trigger of a more major post-bulge earthquake.

Jökulhlaups

In most subglacial eruptions, the water produced from melting ice becomes trapped in a lake between the volcano and the overlying glacier. Eventually this water is released as a violent and potentially dangerous flood. As events of this type are so common in Iceland the Icelanders have coined the term jökulhlaup, which means glacial outburst. One of the most dramatic jökulhlaups to ever occur was a result of an eruption of Grimsvotn in 1996. Over a month, more than $3\,m^3$ of meltwater accumulated beneath the Vatnajökull ice cap. The subglacial lake suddenly burst out, some of the water escaping beneath the ice cap and some spouting out through a side fissure. The resulting flood was temporarily the second biggest flow of water in the world (after the River Amazon). It caused US$14 million of damage and left numerous icebergs scattered across Iceland's southern coastal plain. However, jökulhlaups rarely turn into disasters as they occur in remote unpopulated areas.

Note: **tsunamis** (see p. 80) can occur after catastrophic volcanic eruptions as well as earthquakes, but more rarely so — only 5% of tsunamis are generated by volcanic activity. For example, the structural failure of the volcanic island Krakatoa (VEI 6) in 1883 created a debris flow big enough to produce a tsunami.

Impacts of volcanic hazards on people and the built environment

The impact of volcanic hazards depends on a number of factors, including the **physical profile** of the volcanic event (see p. 64), the status of the volcano — whether it is extinct, dormant or active — as well as key factors such as population density, level of development, standard of governance, timing of eruption, and presence or absence of mitigation strategies.

Environmental impacts at local, regional and global scales (for A-level study)

The **environmental** impacts of explosive volcanic eruptions are largely related to weather and climate, as shown in Table 18.

see p. 64

Define 'active', 'dormant' and 'extinct' volcanoes.

Exam tip

Impacts should be illustrated by 'mini' case studies. These short fact files provide useful supporting evidence in an exam to add locational knowledge to your answer.

Table 18 The effects of large explosive volcanic eruptions on weather and climate

Effect	Mechanism	Begins	Duration	Scale
Increased precipitation	H_2O given off in large quantities during eruption	During eruption	1–4 days, i.e. period of eruption	Local
Reduction of diurnal cycle	Blockage of short-wave and emission of long-wave radiation	Immediately	1–4 days	Local
Reduced tropical precipitation	Blockage of short-wave radiation, reduced evaporation	1–3 months	3–6 months	Regional
Summer cooling of northern hemisphere, tropics and sub-tropics	Blockage of short-wave radiation	1–3 months	1–2 years	Regional
Stratospheric warming	Stratospheric absorption of short-wave and long-wave radiation	1–3 months	1–2 years	Global
Winter warming of northern hemisphere continents	Stratospheric absorption of short-wave and long-wave radiation	6 months	1 or 2 winters	Regional
Global cooling	Blockage of short-wave radiation	Immediately	1–3 years	Global
Global cooling from multiple eruptions	Blockage of short-wave radiation	Immediately	10 years	Global
Ozone depletion, enhanced ultraviolet	Dilution, heterogeneous chemistry and aerosols	1 day	1–2 years	Global

Demographic, economic and social impacts of volcanic hazards on people and the built environment

In general, over a 25 year period, volcanoes are comparatively minor hazards compared with other geo hazards and all natural disasters (Table 19).

Table 19 Average losses per year in natural disasters 1975–2000

	Volcanoes	Earthquakes	All natural disasters
People dead	1,019	18,416	84,034
People injured	285	27,585	65,296
People made homeless	15,128	239,265	4,856,586
People affected	94,399	1,590,314	144 million
Estimated damage (US$ billions)	0.065	21.5	62.0

Volcanic hazards are volcanic events with the potential to cause harm, loss or detriment to humans, and the things humans value.

hazard event × vulnerability of people = adverse consequences, harm or loss

Figure 33 shows a damage table and map for the Nevado del Ruiz eruption, which devastated the local area and the overall economy of Colombia.

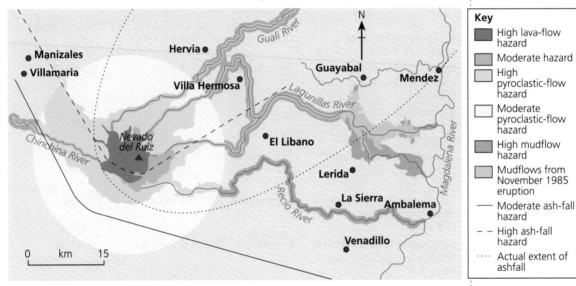

Category of loss	Details
Deaths and injuries	Nearly 70% of the population of Armero killed (20,000 approx.) and a further 17% (5000) injured
Agricultural	60% of the region's livestock, 30% of sorghum and rice crops, and 500,000 bags of coffee destroyed. Over 3400 ha of agricultural land lost from production
Communications	Virtually all roads, bridges, telephone lines and power supplies in the area destroyed. Whole region isolated
Industrial, commercial and civic buildings	50 schools, two hospitals, 58 industrial plants, 343 commercial establishments and the National Coffee Research Centre badly damaged or destroyed
Housing	Most homes destroyed. 8000 people made homeless
Monetary	Cost to the economy estimated at US$7.7 billion, or 20% of the country's GNP for that year

Figure 33 Damage table and map for Nevado del Ruiz, Colombia

Knowledge check 35

Summarise the factors that explain why Nevado del Ruiz was one of the most devastating volcanic hazards.

Exam tip

Always apply your case studies to the specific question — avoid narrative description.

Summary

- Volcanoes can be classified by shape, type of vent and type of eruption. They include shield, composite, cinder cones, fissure eruptions, acid or dome volcanoes and calderas. Eruptions range from explosive to effusive.
- Volcanic processes and associated hazards include pyroclastic flows, lava flows, ash falls, lahars, jökulhlaups, landslides and toxic gases.
- The demographic, economic and social impacts of volcanic hazards depend on physical factors such as the nature of the volcanic event, the status of the volcano, and human factors such as population density, level of development, governance and mitigation strategies.
- Environmental impacts of explosive volcanic eruptions mainly affect weather and climate.
- Volcanic hazards affect people and property and have impacts at global, regional and local scales.
- You will need to learn one (AS) or two (A-level) examples of eruptions to demonstrate the varied degree of risk and impacts of volcanic activity.

Earthquakes, processes, hazards and their impacts

Earthquake characteristics, terminology and causes

Most earthquakes result from movement along fractures or **faults** in rocks. These faults usually occur in groups called a fault zone, which can vary in width from a metre to several kilometres.

Movement occurs along fault planes of all sizes as a result of stresses created by crustal movement. The stresses are not usually released gradually, but build up until they become so great that the rocks shift suddenly along the fault.

- As the fault moves, the shockwaves produced are felt as an earthquake by a process known as **elastic rebound**.
- The point of the break is called the **focus** (or hypocentre), which can be anything from a few kilometres to 700 km deep.
- If the stresses are released in small stages there may be a series of small earthquakes.
- Conversely, if the stresses build up without being released, there is the possibility of a 'Big One' — a major earthquake.

Often, as in the case of Christchurch, many of these faults are buried, so it is difficult to predict earthquakes when there is no knowledge of their existence.

During an earthquake, the extent of ground shaking is measured by motion seismometers activated by strong ground tremors, which record both horizontal and vertical ground accelerations caused by the shaking.

Analysis of data collected from the seismographs shows that earthquakes produce four main types of seismic waves, which are summarised in Table 20.

Table 20 Types of seismic waves

Primary (P) waves	P waves are vibrations caused by compression. They spread out from the earthquake fault at a rate of about 8 km s^{-1} and travel through both solid rock (Earth's core) and liquids (oceans)
Secondary (S) waves	S waves move through the Earth's body at about half the speed of P waves. They vibrate at right angles to the direction of travel. S waves, which cannot travel through liquids, are responsible for a lot of earthquake damage
Rayleigh (R) waves	R waves are surface waves in which particles follow an elliptical path in the direction of propagation and partly in a vertical plane — like water moving with an ocean wave
Love (L) waves	L waves are similar to R waves but move faster and have vibration solely in the horizontal plain. They often generate the greatest damage, as unreinforced masonry buildings cannot cope with horizontal accelerations

The overall severity of an earthquake is dependent on the amplitude and frequency of these wave motions. S and L waves are more destructive than P waves because they have a larger amplitude and force. Therefore, in an earthquake the ground surface may be displaced horizontally, vertically or obliquely, depending on wave activity and geological conditions.

The recorded time intervals between the arrival of the waves at different seismogram stations are used to locate the **epicentre** (the point in the Earth's surface directly above the **focus** of an earthquake).

Three broad categories of earthquake focus, by **depth**, are recognised:

1 deep focus 300–700 km

2 intermediate focus 70–300 km

3 shallow focus 0–70 km. These are the most common (around 75%) and cause the most damage.

Knowledge check 36

Distinguish between the epicentre and focus of an earthquake.

Earthquake processes and hazards

Primary hazards

Ground movement and ground shaking

Surface seismic waves represent the most severe hazard to humans and their activities, since buildings and other structures may collapse and kill or injure their occupants. Ground motion severs underground pipes and power lines, resulting in fires and explosions, especially from escaping gas (1907 San Francisco earthquake). Ruptured water pipes mean that often it is difficult to extinguish these fires.

Near the epicentre, ground motion is both severe and complex, as there is an interlocking pattern of both P and S waves and, theoretically, most damage should occur at the epicentre. Different surface materials respond in different ways to the surface waves, with unconsolidated sediments being most affected because they amplify the shaking. This leads to differential damage of buildings and infrastructure, based not only on distance from the epicentre but also on surface materials (local geological conditions). Steep topography, as in San Francisco, also amplifies 'waves'.

This differential damage was apparent in the Mercalli earthquake intensity levels for the Lomo Prieta earthquake (MM 7.1 in 1988). More than 98% of economic losses were a result of ground shaking, and 41 out of 67 deaths resulted when ground shaking caused the upper tier of the Nimitz freeway in Oakland to collapse because it was constructed on foundations of soft mud and bay fill material.

The phrase 'buildings kill, not earthquakes' is meaningful when considering earthquakes with severe impacts. Building quality is key. Poorly built, unreinforced structures with heavy, tiled roofs are the most dangerous. In the 1988 Armenian earthquake (MM 6.9) 25,000 people were killed, 31,000 were injured and 500,000 were made homeless within a 50 km radius of the epicentre. Distance decay was clearly shown in that 88% of the older stone buildings were destroyed in Spitak, only 5 km from the epicentre, but only 38% in Leninakan, 35 km from the epicentre. However, in Leninakan, 95% of the more modern 9–12 storey Soviet-built pre-cast concrete frame buildings were destroyed (they had soft foundations and no earthquake proofing). In the 2008 Sichuan earthquake (MM 7.9), although the ground shaking formed a linear pattern extending along the Longmen Shan Fault, a large number of pre-cast concrete school buildings were completely destroyed, scattered over a wide area, with other buildings remaining comparatively unaffected. This hit the headlines because, as a result of China's one-child policy, many families lost their only child.

The **duration** of shaking is also important — longer periods of shaking causing more damage for the same magnitude event.

Secondary hazards

Liquefaction

Liquefaction is an important secondary hazard that is associated with loose sediments. This is the process by which water-saturated material can lose strength and behave as a fluid when subjected to strong ground shaking which increases pore water pressures. Poorly compacted sands and silts situated at depths less than 10 m below the surface are most affected when saturated with water.

In the earthquakes at Christchurch, New Zealand (2010), Mexico City (1985) and Valdez Alaska (1964) liquefaction that caused buildings and infrastructure to collapse was a notable hazard, resulting in an almost random pattern of building destruction.

Landslides, rock and snow avalanches

Severe ground shaking causes natural slopes to weaken and fail. The resulting landslides, rock and snow avalanches can make a major contribution to earthquake disasters, especially in mountain areas such as the Himalayas. These landslides hamper relief efforts, as in the Kashmir earthquake or the Nepal Gorkha earthquake in 2015. It is estimated that landslides can double earthquake deaths, especially with high magnitude earthquakes because they can occur over a huge area.

Landslide risk post-earthquake varies with differences in topography, rainfall, soil and land use (whether forested or not). An example of an earthquake-generated rock slide occurred in Peru in 1970 as a massive rock avalanche broke away from the overhanging face of the Huascaran Mountain. A turbulent flow of mud and boulders flowed down the Santa valley, forming a wave 50 m high, travelling at an average speed of 70–100 m s^{-1}. The towns of Yungay and Ranatirca were buried under debris 10 m deep, killing 18,000 people in four minutes. Flooding can occur, as it did in

> **Knowledge check 37**
>
> Explain how China's one-child policy exacerbated the tragedy of the Sichuan earthquake.

Sichuan when numerous landslides dammed temporary lakes which subsequently burst through, causing flash flooding. The recent aftershocks of earthquakes in central Italy generated avalanches after heavy snow.

Tsunamis

Tsunamis are the most destructive secondary earthquake-related hazard. Most tsunamis are generated at subduction–convergent plate boundaries, with 90% of damaging tsunamis occurring in the Pacific Basin (hence the establishment of the Pacific Warning System). Exceptions include the 2004 Boxing Day tsunami in the Indian Ocean. The most active tsunami source area is the Japan–Taiwan islands (over 25% of tsunamis).

Tsunamis occur if an earthquake rupture occurs under the ocean or in a coastal zone, if the focus is not deep within the Earth's crust, and if the magnitude of the earthquake (6+) is large enough to create significant vertical displacement. A tsunami is a series of ocean waves that 'spread out' from the earthquake focus, carrying large volumes of water, and debris too once they reach land.

> **Knowledge check 38**
>
> Explain why only certain earthquakes cause tsunamis.

The intensity (magnitude) of tsunamis can be measured by a descriptive, observational scale devised by Soloviev in 1978, which is based on the run-up height.

In the last 100 years, more than 2000 tsunamis have killed over 500,000 people (over 50% in the mega disaster of the 2004 Boxing Day tsunami, which was the most deadly tsunami recorded).

A number of physical factors influence the degree of devastation, including wave energy, which is dependent on water depth, the process of shoaling, the shape of the coastline, the topography of the land and the presence or absence of natural defences such as coral reefs or mangroves. Human factors include the population profile, the degree of coastal development, the cohesiveness of the society and people's experience of the tsunami hazard, as well as the presence or absence of warning systems and evacuation plans.

1 **Generation in deep ocean**

2 **Tsunami run-up**: nature of the waves depends on
(i) cause of the wave, e.g. earthquake or volcanic eruption
(ii) distance travelled from source
(iii) water depth over route
(iv) offshore topography and coastline shape

3 **Landfall**: impact will depend on physical factors and land uses, population density and warning given
Waves radiate from the source in all directions

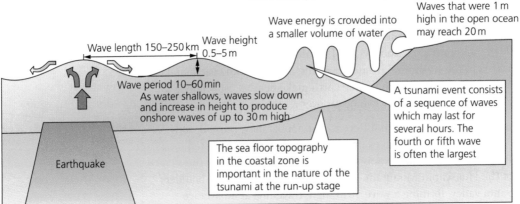

Figure 34 The formation and key features of a tsunami

Demographic, economic and social impacts of earthquakes on people and the built environment

There are a number of differences between the impacts of volcanoes and earthquakes with their related tsunamis. In comparison with volcanoes, earthquakes can be much more deadly and their impacts more selective in terms of damage to buildings and deaths of people.

The **primary** effects of a major earthquake are the immediate consequences, such as damage to houses from shaking or fires, and instantaneous deaths of people hit by falling tiles and roofs. On the streets, cracks form across roads and bridges collapse; there is widespread destruction of gas mains and water pipes; and severe fractures of or the concertina downwards of badly built concrete high-rise blocks. Within a few minutes people are trapped and injured; many die quickly.

The **secondary** effects of an earthquake are those that manifest in the days, weeks and even months after an earthquake event. Air pollution might result from burning fires and combustion from leaking gas mains. Contamination from sewage is another serious secondary danger, causing diseases such as typhoid or cholera as a result of a shortage of clean water. After the 2010 Haiti earthquake 738,979 cases of cholera were reported, leading to 421,410 hospitalisations and nearly 10,000 deaths. As railroad and telephone links are cut and airports are damaged, the lack of supply lines for rescue and recovery is another secondary consequence (a major problem following both the Haiti and Kashmir earthquakes).

How people cope and how quickly they can get back on their feet largely depends on whether the earthquake occurs in a high income country, where there are contingency plans for all stages of the hazard management cycle underpinned by financial support mainly from within the country. In low income countries there are fewer resources for rescue and recovery, and a reliance on international aid.

The secondary effects have both social and economic consequences. Many factories and offices are so damaged that work cannot resume for some considerable time, costing money in wages, lost production, future orders and exports. The community might also be threatened by hunger and disease and possibly by social disorder from looting etc. as people desperately seek to survive.

In rural areas, farmland and crops will be seriously affected if drainage or irrigation systems are disrupted and fields covered in rubble. Where landslides have blocked roads, farmers are not able to get their products to market. On the other hand, in urban areas the effects can be extremely severe because of the high density of buildings and the high value of the infrastructure. If buildings are completely destroyed, leaving large areas of derelict land, uncollected refuse and decomposing organic material can result in infestations of rats and flies. The Tohoku earthquake of 2010 had exceptionally severe secondary effects as a result of the 'triple whammy' of earthquake, tsunami and the resultant nuclear disaster.

Exam tip

Always keep up to date. April 2016 had two serious earthquakes, in Ecuador and Japan. Both will make interesting research.

Summary

- Earthquake characteristics include a focus, epicentre, depth and different types of waves (P, S, L and R waves).
- Earthquakes result from movement along fractures or **faults** in rocks and create different types of hazards including ground shaking (intensity and duration), liquefaction, landslides, avalanches and tsunamis.
- Demographic, economic and social impacts of earthquakes result from both primary and secondary causes.
- Earthquakes affect people and property and have impacts at global, regional and local scales.
- You will need to learn one (AS) or two (A-level) examples of an earthquake to demonstrate the varied degree of risk and impacts of earthquake activity.

Human factors affecting risk and vulnerability

Disaster versus hazard

A disaster is the realisation of a hazard 'which causes a significant impact on a vulnerable population'. While the terms 'hazard' and 'disaster' are often used casually or synonymously, there is a major distinction between them, which is shown clearly by the Degg model (Figure 35).

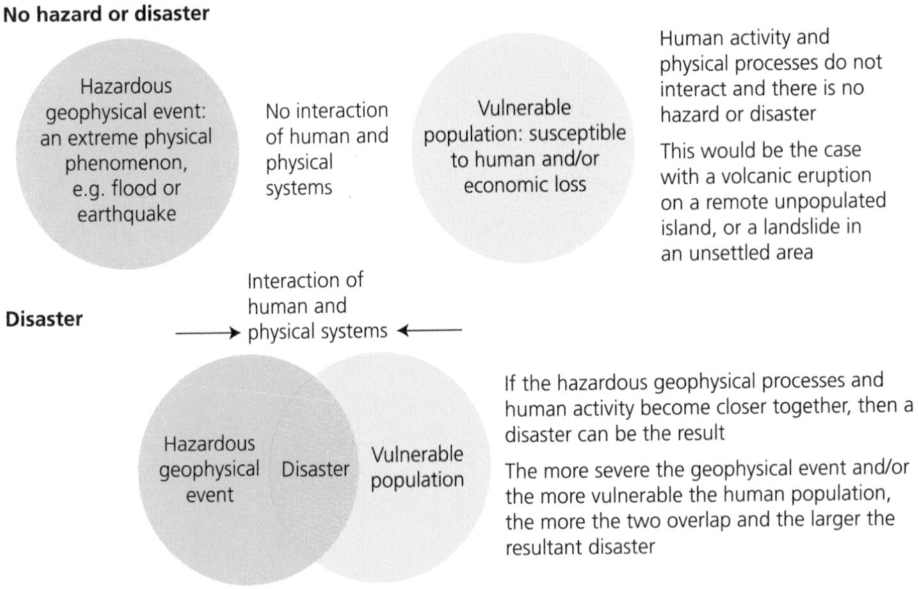

Figure 35 The Degg model

Risk

Risk is defined as 'the probability of a hazard occurring and creating loss of lives and livelihoods'. It might be assumed that risk of exposure to tectonic hazards is involuntary, but in reality people consciously place themselves at risk for a variety of reasons, including:

- the unpredictability of hazards: areas may not have experienced a hazard in living memory
- the changing risk over time (e.g. a perceived extinct volcano)
- lack of alternative locations to live, especially for the poor
- an assessment that economic benefits outweigh the costs, e.g. for areas of rich volcanic soils or of great tourism potential
- optimistic perceptions of hazard risks: it can all be solved by the technofix, or it won't happen to me

The risk is altered by human conditions and actions, for example two similar-magnitude earthquakes (Lomo Prieta, California and Bam, Iran) had very different consequences because the people in Bam (poorer in a developing country) were generally at much greater risk, i.e. they were more **vulnerable**.

Vulnerability

Vulnerability implies a high risk of exposure to hazard, combined with an inability to cope. In human terms this is the degree of resistance offered by a social system to the impact of a hazardous event. This depends on the **resilience** of individuals and communities, the reliability of management systems and the quality of governance that have been put in place.

Certain conditions amplify vulnerability.

The risk equation

The risk equation measures the level of hazard risk for an area:

$$risk = \frac{\text{frequency and/or magnitude of hazard} \times \text{level of vulnerability}}{\text{capacity of population to cope (i.e. resilience level)}}$$

While the **intrinsic** physical properties of a hazard event profile can lay the foundations for the development of a disaster, it is the **extrinsic** areal or local factors that impact on the vulnerability of communities and societies and cause tectonic disasters. It is also to do with the actual communities and societies themselves.

The PAR model (Figure 36) helps to explain the variability in levels of vulnerability and resistance. It is this vulnerability (both human and economic) not the tectonic environment that helps to explain the differences in the severity of the social and economic impacts of physically similar hazard events (see Table 21).

As the PAR model shows, certain drivers of disaster (root causes) result in pressures that create potentially unsafe conditions. The development paradigm argues that, at a macro-scale, the root causes of vulnerability lie in the contrasting economic and political systems of the developed/developing divide. The most vulnerable people are channelled into the most hazardous environments (the result of chronic malnutrition, disease, armed conflict, chaotic and ineffective governance, lack of educational empowerment). Therefore the risk equation is being increased because levels of vulnerability are increasing and resilience is decreasing.

Knowledge check 39

Choose three examples of tectonic hazard events where people have exacerbated the scale of the disaster by putting themselves at risk.

Knowledge check 40

Explain how unsustainable development can increase the risk equation.

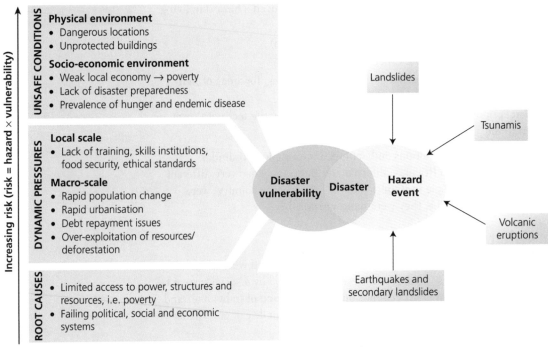

Figure 36 The PAR (pressure and release) model

Table 21 Differences in the severity of social and economic impacts of physically similar hazard events

		Magnitude	Fatalities	Damage US$ millions
1992	Erzican, Turkey	6.8	540	3,000
1999	Izmit, Turkey	7.4	17,225	12,000
1989	Loma Prieta, USA	7.1	68	10,000
1994	Northridge, USA	6.8	61	44,000

Drivers of disaster and vulnerability

Economic factors

Human vulnerability is closely associated with levels of absolute poverty and the economic gap between rich and poor (inequality). Disasters are exacerbated by poverty (Haiti, Kashmir etc.). The poorest least developed countries (LDCs) lack money to invest in education, social services, basic infrastructure and technology, all of which help communities overcome disasters. Poor countries lack effective infrastructure. Economic growth increases economic assets and therefore raises risk unless managed effectively. However, developed countries can invest in technology for disaster reduction and production, and aid after the hazard event.

Technological factors

While community preparedness and education can prove vital in mitigating disasters, technological solutions can play a major role, especially in building design and prevention and protection and also in the design of monitoring equipment (see p. 87).

Social factors

World population is growing, especially in developing nations where there are higher levels of urbanisation and many people live in dense concentrations in unsafe political settings. It is not only the density of a population but also the population profile (age, gender and levels of education) that are significant. An increasingly ageing population, as in China (Sichuan), increases vulnerability with problems of emergency evacuation and survival. Housing conditions and quality of building have a major impact on the scale of deaths and injuries. Essentially, disadvantaged people are more likely to die, suffer injury and psychological trauma during the recovery and reconstruction phase because they live in poorer housing which is not earthquake proof.

In the Sichuan and Kashmir earthquakes, badly built schools led to disproportionate deaths amongst the young.

Political factors

The lack of strong central government produces a weak organisational structure. Equally, a lack of financial institutions inhibits disaster mitigation and both emergency and post-disaster recovery. A good strong central government leads to highly efficient rescue (Chinese earthquake). Haiti is a classic case of the cumulative impacts of poor quality governance over many years.

Geographical factors

Geographical factors can be highly significant and case-study-specific, such as location (rural, urban, coast), degrees of isolation and time of day.

- Increasing urbanisation, with poorly sited squatter settlements, especially in mega cities, creates high hazard risk and exposure. These huge cities are vulnerable to post-earthquake fires (Kobe).
- Destruction of rural environments can result in disasters among rural populations, with a loss of food supplies and livelihoods (2015 Nepal Gorkha earthquake).
- Relief, rescue and recovery efforts are difficult in some areas (Kashmir, where isolation, the cold climate and frontier position complicated relief and recovery).
- The geography may lead to multi-hazard hotspots where the impacts of earthquakes, tsunamis or volcanic eruptions are amplified by impacts of other hazards.
- Timing of the first earthquake and aftershocks (e.g. Christchurch 2010–11 and Italy 2016–17) have a major effect, especially on social impacts such as deaths.

Knowledge check 41

Define the term 'multi-hazard hotspot'.

Summary

- Economic factors affecting risk and vulnerability include level of development, level of technology, inequality and poverty.
- Social factors include population density, population profile (age, gender), housing conditions, quality of building and levels of education.
- Political factors include the quality of governance and strength of central government.
- Geographical factors include rural–urban location, time of day and degree of isolation.

Responses to tectonic hazards

Monitoring, **predicting** and **warning** of tectonic hazards are examples of modifying people's **vulnerability** to the hazard — this also includes community preparedness and land use planning.

Prediction buys time to:

- warn people to evacuate
- prepare for a hazard event
- manage impacts more effectively
- help insurance companies assess risk
- prioritise government spending
- help decision makers carry out cost–benefit calculations of, for example, building expensive hi-tech systems

When?
- **Recurrence intervals** — an indication of longer-term risk
- **Seasonality** — climatic and geo-morphic hazards may have seasonal patterns, e.g. Atlantic hurricanes occur from June to November
- **Timing** — the hardest to predict, both in the long term (e.g. winter gales) and the short term (e.g. time of hurricane)

Where?
- **Regional scale** — easy to predict, e.g. plate boundaries, 'tornado alley', drought zones
- **Local scale** — more difficult, except for fixed-point hazards, e.g. floods, volcanoes, coastal erosion
- **Moving hazards** — extremely difficult, e.g. hurricane tracking

What?
- **Type of hazard** — many areas can be affected by more than one hazard; purpose of forecast is to predict what type of hazard might occur
- **Magnitude of hazard** — important in anticipating impacts and managing a response
- **Primary vs secondary impacts** — some hazards have 'multiple' natures; earthquakes may cause liquefaction, volcanoes may cause lahars

Hazard prediction

Why?
- **Reduce deaths** — by enabling evaluation
- **Reduce damage** — by enabling preparation
- **Enhance management** — by enabling cost–benefit calculations and risk assessment
- **Improve understanding** — by testing models against reality
- **Allow preparedness plans to be put in operation** — by individuals, local government, national agencies

Who?
- **Tell all?** — fair, but risks over-warning, scepticism and panic
- **Tell some?** — for example, emergency services, but may cause rumours and mistrust
- **Tell none?** — useful to test predictions, but difficult to justify

How?
- **Past records** — enable recurrence intervals to be estimated
- **Monitoring (physical)** — monitored and recorded using ground-based methods or, for climatic and volcanic hazards, remote sensing
- **Monitoring (human)** — factors influencing human vulnerability (e.g. incomes, exchange rates, unemployment); human impacts (e.g. deforestation)

Figure 37 The importance of hazard prediction

Monitoring, prediction and warning of earthquakes

Predicting earthquakes would allow people to evacuate the danger area before the event, but unfortunately this is only a seismologist's dream.

On a global scale, the regions of risk can be identified. At a **regional** scale, previous magnitude and frequency data can be used to pinpoint areas of risk and predict the **probabilities** of an earthquake occurring, but not precisely when this might happen. As an earthquake results from the release of strain building up in the crustal rocks, the areas which have 'loaded' for some time are likely to move in the future.

Seismologists in California have produced earthquake probability maps for major fault lines such as San Andreas based on this 'gap theory'.

At a local scale, attempts to predict earthquakes a few hours before the event are based on diaries of survivors (living histories) and the results from monitoring equipment. This includes changes in groundwater levels, release of radon gas or even (often used in China) unusual animal behaviour. These changes are thought to be due to ground dilation and rock cracking just before an earthquake. While the 1975 Heichang earthquake was successfully forecast 5½ hours before the event, allowing 90,000 people to be successfully evacuated, the Chinese failed to forecast the Great Tangshan earthquake of 1976 (an intra-plate earthquake), which was totally unexpected and resulted in a huge death toll.

Figure 38 shows a range of possible monitoring methods which could be used to explore earthquake processes.

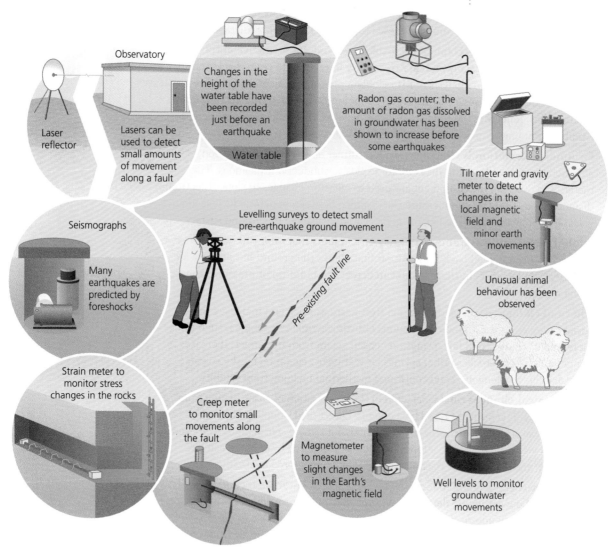

Figure 38 Monitoring methods for predicting an earthquake along an active fault line

It is possible to produce earthquake risk maps, which predict the likely impact of an earthquake on a particular designated area. These maps are based on known factors such as rock types, ground shaking, hill slopes, liquefaction danger and landslide potential. GIS are being used to develop this system further, especially by mapping concealed faults.

Monitoring, prediction and warning of volcanic eruptions

Given adequate monitoring, warning of certain volcanic eruptive phases is possible, making adaptive responses such as education, community preparation and emergency evacuation procedures feasible.

Most volcanic eruptions are preceded by a variety of environmental changes that accompany the rise of magma to the surface (i.e. precursors to an eruption). Unfortunately, it is very difficult to predict the precise temporal occurrence of the actual eruption reaching danger levels. Moreover, for highly explosive eruptions, many of the phenomena are not present, and the precise timing of these eruptions is highly unpredictable.

1   **Earthquake activity** is common near volcanoes and, for predictive purposes, it is important to measure any increase in activity in relation to usual background levels. This requires an analysis of historic data plus supplementary field data from portable seismometers. Warning signs include a swarm of higher frequency earthquakes, reflecting the fracture of local rocks as magnetic pressure increases. Audible rumblings can sometimes be heard using sound instruments.

2   **Ground deformation** is sometimes the forerunner of an explosive eruption, although it can be difficult to measure for explosive subduction volcanoes. Tilt meters and other survey equipment are used to measure changes in slope. Electronic distance meters (EDM) can measure the distance between benchmarks placed on a volcano to pinpoint when the magma is rising and displacing the ground surface.

3   **Global positioning systems** (GPS) rely on satellites that orbit the Earth twice a day and constantly feed back information that allows the ground base to provide profiles. GPS receivers in the volcano can detect the build-up of pressure from rising magma.

4   **Thermal changes** occur as the magma rises to the surface and increases the surface temperature. Ground observations of hydrothermal phenomena, such as increased discharge from hot springs, increased steam from fumaroles, increases in temperature of crater lakes or hot springs, or wilting of vegetation on the volcanic slope, can be supplemented and confirmed by thermal imaging from satellites.

5   **Geochemical changes** can be detected in the composition of gases issuing from volcanic vents (increasing SO_2 or H_2S content). Direct field sampling of gases escaping from surface vents is the usual method, but remote sensing has been used too. SO_2 injected high into the atmosphere can be measured by onboard satellite equipment, and behaviour of volcanic plumes can be monitored by weather satellites.

6   **Lahars** have been monitored for years by local people but more recently videocams allow automatic detection systems. Seismometers detect ground vibrations from an approaching lahar, so an emergency message can be transmitted downslope to population centres, enabling short-term warnings and emergency evacuation.

Although there is no fully reliable forecasting and warning system, some success has been achieved in limiting deaths. For example, Phivolcs is a successful scheme developed in the Philippines to monitor the most active volcanoes in the most densely populated areas.

Once a volcano has erupted, for example the one in Montserrat, a danger zone is then delineated. Once clear warnings of new volanic activity are received, people are evacuated from the danger zone. The community is prepared in advance on evacuation routes and temporary food and shelter are supplied. However, the length of time available for evacuation is unpredictable, and sometimes there are false alarms. For example, in Montserrat, 5000 residents were evacuated three times between December 1995 and August 1996. In the Bay of Naples, home to Vesuvius, 700,000 people living in major cities such as Naples, are at risk from its eruption. Volcanologists and civil defence officials have drawn up an emergency evacuation plan. The operation is huge and even involves moving people to safety by ship with detailed routes carefully planned. Also, volcanic risk maps, using three grades of hazard risk, have to be created for a variety of hazards such as pyroclastic flows and ash falls. However, evacuation strategies, if managed effectively, can save thousands of lives.

Prediction and warning of tsunamis

Modifying the vulnerability is the main response to tsunamis. Scientists can predict a possible tsunami by monitoring earthquake activity, with the aim of issuing warnings to vulnerable populations who can evacuate the area. Tsunami forecasting and warning systems are well established in the Pacific, although frequent false alarms can lead to threat denial and financial loss.

Global-scale warning systems

In 1948 the Pacific Warning System for 24 Pacific Basin nations was established, with its centre near Honolulu in Hawaii. Seismic stations detect all the earthquakes and their events are interpreted to check for tsunami risk. The aim is to alert all areas at risk within 1 hour. The time it takes for a wave to travel across the Pacific allows ample time to warn shipping and evacuate low-lying coastal areas. As not all earthquakes result in tsunamis, it is a difficult decision whether to issue a warning. If the earthquake is larger than 7.5 (MMS) all locations within 3 hours' 'travel time' of the tsunami waves are put on warning alert to evacuate the coast, with areas 3–6 hours away put on standby.

There was no Indian Ocean Warning System in place for the 2004 Boxing Day tsunami, although one has subsequently been developed, based in Indonesia and India.

Regional-scale warning systems

Regional-scale warning systems aim to respond to locally generated tsunamis with short warning times as these pose a much greater threat. Ninety per cent of tsunamis occur within 400 km of the source area, so there may be less than 30 minutes between tsunami formation and landfall.

Japan has the most developed system — the target is to issue a warning within 20 minutes of the approach of a **tsunamigenic** earthquake within 600 km of the Japanese coastline. Such a warning was issued for the Tohoku earthquake of 2011, but the height of the tsunami wall failed to protect from the 40 m high waves. In 1994 a new detector and computer system was set up so that wave heights and arrival times could be more rapidly transmitted.

There are three main difficulties to overcome. First, the tsunami may destroy power and communication lines; second, as at Aceh, Indonesia in 2004, events many occur too quickly to issue a warning. Third, warnings must be supported by effective land-based evacuation routes and community education.

Mitigation and adaptation of tectonic hazards

A useful framework for classifying responses to tectonic hazards, developed by K. Smith, divides them into three categories:

1 modify the event
2 modify the vulnerability
3 modify the loss

Modify the event

While little can be done to control most volcanic hazards, some progress has been made in controlling lava flows. Seawater surges were successfully used to cool and solidify the lava flows during the 1973 Eldafell eruption in Iceland, and stop it advancing on the harbour of Vestmannaeyjar. Explosives have been used with some success on Mt Etna in Sicily to create artificial barriers to divert lava flows away from villages in the 1983, 1991 and 2001 eruptions.

Some attempts have been made to modify the impact of the tsunami hazard by hazard-resistant design. Defensive engineering works provide some protection, and the trend now is for a combination of hard engineering, using onshore walls for high value urban areas, and the redevelopment of natural protection provided by coral reefs and mangroves for rural areas.

Being able to control the physical variables of an earthquake, such as duration of shaking, is unlikely in the foreseeable future, although human-induced earthquakes such as those caused by dam construction or fracking could be prevented by not allowing development in areas subject to seismic hazards.

The main way of modifying an earthquake event is by **hazard-resistant building design** to develop **aseismic** (earthquake-resistant) buildings, as the collapse of buildings is responsible for the majority of deaths, injuries and economic losses. There is no clear relationship between building age and damage, although recent quakes have shown that specially designed, high-specification aseismic buildings in California and Japan do perform well even in high magnitude earthquakes.

There are currently three main types of building using the techno fix of expensive aseismic designs. These are ideal for important public buildings, key services such as hospitals and utilities such as power stations, but they are too expensive for homes. This is important as 70% of the world's 100 largest cities (12.5% of the world's population) are exposed to significant earthquake hazards once every 50 years.

Level of development is a key factor, as only economically developed nations can afford to **enforce** the strict seismic and building codes that can reduce death rates. In many developing or emerging nations there may be notional codes, but there is corruption and little money or political will to enforce them, hence the significant collapse of school buildings in the Sichuan earthquake. Recently, low-cost aseismic buildings suitable for rural and urban areas have been designed using cheap local materials such as wood and wattle and daub, and avoiding materials such as concrete lintels and corrugated iron, which cause death and injury.

Two problems with this approach are that (i) as in Christchurch, New Zealand, many older buildings need 'retrofitting' to bring them up to current higher standards of earthquake-resistant design, and (ii) damage is often from a variety of causes, not just shaking.

Modify the vulnerability

In addition to prediction, warning and monitoring other key parts of this strategy include land use planning and zoning, community preparedness and education.

Land use planning and layout is crucial in mitigating the severity of impacts of all three tectonic hazards.

- Tectonic hazard risk maps identify the most hazardous areas, which can be regulated by building codes. Lessons learned from **major earthquakes** are incorporated into planning new developments or rebuilding.
- Avoiding overly high density urban squatter settlements and providing public open space creates safe areas away from fires and aftershock damage. Considerable thought also needs to be given to the siting of public buildings, which should be preferably scattered in areas of low risk to reduce the chances of the total collapse of services (part of Tokyo planning).
- In areas of **volcanic hazard** risk maps are deployed (though few are available in developing countries). However, in areas such as Hawaii, lava flow hazards have been mapped and can be used as the basis for informed land use planning, avoiding valleys where flows are concentrated.
- In **tsunami-prone** areas, rezoning of low-lying coastal land can be an excellent defence. For example, in Crescent City, California, following tsunami damage from the 1964 Alaskan earthquake, the waterfront has been turned into public parks, and businesses moved to higher ground back from the shore.

Community preparedness and education are the core strategy of any programme to modify the vulnerability of people to tectonic hazard. Many volcanic events are preceded by clear warning of activity. Preparation of the community through education about precursors to look for, how to evacuate an area and how to develop resistance is key.

Community preparedness for seismic hazards is centred on preparing the general public to cope, and the emergency services and government to manage before, during and after the event. Experience as to how people behave in earthquakes has helped to devise recommendations for appropriate action and earthquake drills are now widely publicised.

In California, there is increased emphasis on using **smart technology** to prepare the emergency services.

Knowledge check 42

List the precursors communities should be made aware of.

Modify the loss

Essentially this has two major facets: **aid** and **insurance**. **Insurance** is mainly available in economically richer nations. The vast majority of people at risk from tectonic hazards do not have access to affordable insurance. It is largely commercial and industrial property that is insured against tectonic risk and disaster damage.

Insurance is a key strategy for economically developed countries. However, while individuals realise that the benefits of purchasing an insurance policy are enormous and could outweigh costs of damage, insurers who are wary of huge payouts following major hazard events assess the risk and charge accordingly. They also force householders to take preventative measures such as refitting their houses. Private properties become uninsurable in high risk areas and for poorer people, leading to governments taking over provision in some instances.

Humanitarian concern for disaster victims results in **emergency aid** flowing in from governments, NGOs and private donations. Aid is used at all stages of the hazard management cycle (see Figure 39) for relief, rehabilitation and reconstruction.

Short-term and long-term responses to the effects of earthquake and volcanic hazards

There are two useful frameworks that can be used to look at responses over time.

1 The **Hazard Disaster Management Cycle** (Figure 39) identifies a number of phases in the management of a hazard from immediate response, through rehabilitation, to recovery and the development of resilience via mitigation strategies. Various versions of the cycle show how the strategies of modify the loss, modify the event and modify human vulnerability fit in the cycle. Today technology is of increasing importance in the management of all stages of the cycle.

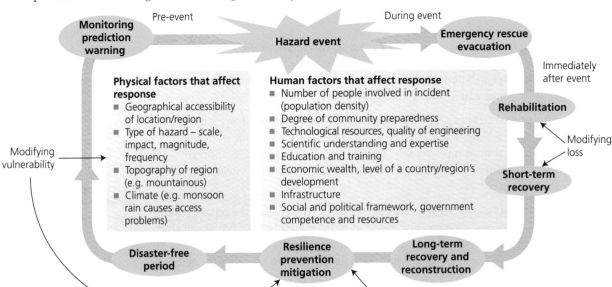

Figure 39 The Hazard Disaster Management Cycle

2 **Park's disaster-response curve** (Figure 40) allows modelling of the impact of a disaster from pre-disaster, through the impact, to post-disaster recovery, and shows the importance of various strategies over the lifecycle of a hazard event.

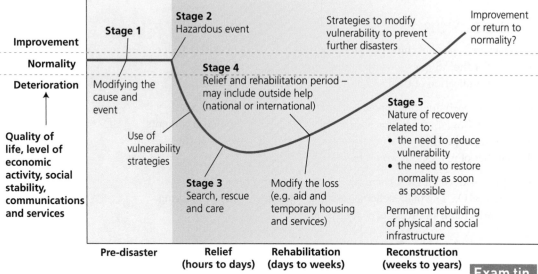

Figure 40 Park's disaster-response curve model

Summary

- Monitoring, predicting and warning of tectonic hazards are ways of modifying the vulnerability of populations.
- Prediction can be effective for volcanic hazards but is almost impossible for earthquakes.
- Short-term responses to the effects of earthquake and volcanic hazards include prediction and warning, national and international emergency aid.
- Long-term responses include hazard-resistant building design, land use planning, community preparedness, education and insurance.
- The Hazard Disaster Management Cycle shows how the choice of response depends on complex and interrelated physical and human factors.

Questions & Answers

About this section

The questions below are typical of the style and structure that you can expect to see in the exam papers. For the AS questions, the number of lines given in the exam answer booklet are an indication of the level of detail required.

There are comments on each question, preceded by **e**, which offer guidance on question interpretation. Student responses are then provided, with detailed comments for each answer, preceded by **e**, indicating the strengths and weaknesses of the answer and the number of marks that would be awarded.

The examiners have a grid which gives them the maximum marks for each Assessment Objective (AO). The mark scheme includes indicative content, marking guidance and, for marks totals in excess of 5, marks bands.

■ Coastal landscapes

Question 1 (Eduqas style)

Study Figure 41.

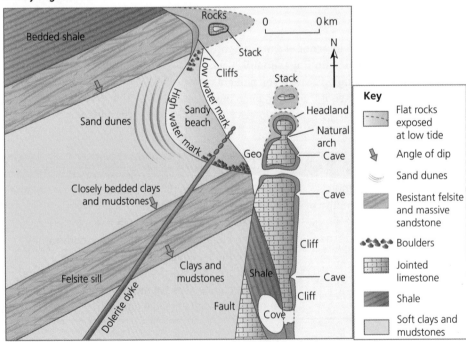

Figure 41

(a) Define the terms 'structure' and 'lithology'. (5 marks)

(b) Assess the impact of structure and lithology on the landforms shown. (15 marks)

🄮 In (a) be precise with your definitions and be careful to extend the definition if the question is worth several marks. Part (b) requires you to demonstrate your ability to develop a sustained line of reasoning that is coherent, relevant, substantiated and logically structured. It is always worth planning your answer, either by landform or under the headings of structure and lithology.

Student answer

(a) Structure is the geological disposition of the rocks ✓, whether the beds are horizontal, vertical or dipping ✓. It includes the degree of folding and faulting ✓ and the incidence of jointing ✓.

Lithology is the physical and chemical make-up of the rock ✓. It includes the hardness of the rock ✓, its mineral composition ✓ or its stability ✓.

🄮 Remember, 1 mark is awarded for a basic statement, a further mark for extension and amplification (max 5 marks in this case).

(b) The coastline shown has a varied plan. In the northeastern area there are headlands and bays with the headlands having steep cliffs as massive abrasion has led to their recession, forming extensive shore platforms.

The clays have been eroded to form a large bay with a sandy beach — onshore winds have blown the sand up to form sand dunes. At either end of the beach are piles of boulders that have fallen from the cliffs. A prominent feature is the ridge formed by the dolerite dyke. In the east of the map the main rock is limestone. A range of micro-features, such as caves, arches and stacks have formed. The initial feature is the cave that develops into an arch and when the roof of the arch collapses a sea stack forms. You can see how the sea has broken through the wall of limestone to hollow out a cave whose width is elongated by the easily eroded shale.

🄮 **2/15 marks awarded** While the main landforms are described and a basic knowledge of processes is shown, there is no attempt to look at the impact of structure and lithology, except at a superficial level — for example, ideas of weaker rock — and certainly no mention of assessment of the importance of the impacts of structure and lithology. There is little development and no exemplification. This answer would probably achieve at most at the top Band 1 for AO1 and 0 for AO2, since there is no assessment or evaluation.

This may seem harsh for a reasonable description of many of the landforms, but it is vital that you are familiar with the Assessment Objectives for each style of question. It is also important to identify the key terms and command words before you begin.

Questions & Answers

AO1 content demonstrates knowledge and understanding of the coastal landforms shown. Always try to include examples of landforms, for example, along the Dorset coast. Always use geographical vocabulary and locate the features on the geological map.

Possible points to include (the indicative content) are as follows.

- A fault divides the discordant coast to the northwest, which dips southeast from a concordant coast in the east (cf. the Heritage Coast in Dorset).
- Lithology leads to differential erosion of the discordant coast to produce headlands and bays.
- The concordant coast shows the stages of cave formation from incipient feature to full cave.
- The resistant rocks form cliffs with shore platforms resulting from recession after abrasion.
- A dolerite dyke forms a resistant feature on the sandy beach.
- A geo is eroded along the fault.
- Micro-features of caves, arches and stacks are well displayed in the jointed limestone.

AO2 allows you to demonstrate application of your knowledge and understanding by assessing the distinctive impact of structure and lithology on the landforms shown. Both are likely to be important. Try to develop a logical order that looks at scale from macro- (the coastline in plan) through to micro-scale features such as caves, arches and stacks. Remember that, to access the higher mark bands, you need to *assess* the impact, weighing up the importance and role of structure and lithology.

Indicative content:

- Structure (the way the rocks are disposed) is responsible for the 'big picture' for a discordant coast composed of rocks of varying lithology, forming headlands and bays, and the concordant limestone coast of uniform lithology, until this is breached and the cove is scooped out of the shale.
- The varying hardness and solubility, i.e. the lithology, is responsible for features at a smaller scale.
- The micro-features of the cliff architecture are formed by solution and erosion of the jointed limestone, which shows caves, arches and stacks.
- The massive sandstone is resistant to erosion and forms cliffs above a shore platform.
- The fault, another structural feature, is a zone of weakness and has been eroded to form a geo (a fault-guided inlet).
- The resistant dyke, which is intruded into the existing strata, forms a ridge on the sandy bay.

Possible conclusion: Overall, structure would seem to have the greatest impact, with lithology responsible for many features as a result of differential erosion.

Question 2 (WJEC AS style)

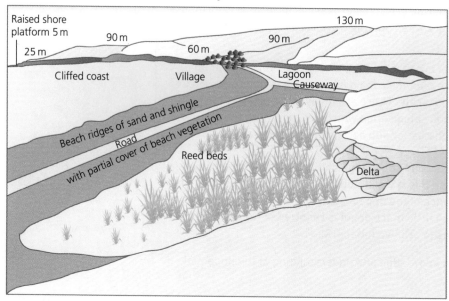

Figure 42

Assess the contribution of changes in sea level to the landforms shown in Figure 42.

(8 marks, AO1 5, AO2 3)

ⓔ You are required to demonstrate your ability to develop a sustained line of reasoning on the contribution of a process in a relevant, coherent, substantiated and logically structured way.

Student answer

Changes in sea level have over the millions of years had a significant impact on a wide scale.

You can see a number of marine erosion levels at 130 m, 90 m and 60 m as well as a raised shore platform at around 5–10 m above present-day sea level. These marine erosion surfaces indicate heights of the former sea bed and show the impact of a combination of isostatic warping at a local scale and eustatic falls in sea level, which operate globally and are associated with expansion of ice masses during the glacial (icehouse) process which occurred in the Pleistocene. Changes of sea level may also have been responsible for the formation of the bay bar, a shingle bar forming across the bay which created the lagoon.

There are many theories associated with the formation of bars with all looking at the role of changing sea levels. Bars in South Carolina are associated with an emerging coastline.

The formation of the bar creates a fossil or relict cliff line which cannot be eroded by the current marine erosion, so is subject only to subaerial erosion and will become degraded — so this is an example of a declining contribution.

> The bar itself was almost certainly formed by a combination of longshore drift and constructive waves and marine erosional processes have clearly formed a cliff line. Longshore drift occurs when oblique waves are refracted and material is moved along shore.
>
> So it can be seen that changes in sea level have a very wide impact spatially with a range of features formed but their main importance is their own level operation over such a long time scale. There are many other processes such as marine erosion or vegetation colonisation which are modifying the features currently such as stabilising the bar or sub aerial erosion of the fossil cliff line.

(e) **7/8 marks awarded** There is good knowledge and understanding shown of features over geological time so this is worth full AO1 marks. There is also a fair attempt to assess the importance of the impact of changes in sea level which would score 2 marks for AO2. A little more detail is required of the other relevant factors affecting the landforms to achieve full marks.

AO1 content is concerned with knowledge and understanding of the impact of changes in sea level.

Indicative content AO1:

■ A series of coastal erosion platforms/surfaces at 130 m, 90 m, 60 m and 25 m as well as a raised shore platform at 5 m suggest a major relative fall in sea level over geologic time.
■ Many bay bars are associated with emerging coastlines.
■ Constructive wave action may have contributed to the bay bar development. Destructive waves have formed a line of cliffs, some of which are now fossil cliffs, as they are cut off from the present-day marine action by the bar.

To achieve the AO2 marks you need to apply your knowledge and understanding of the significance of changes in sea level in contributing to the landscape as a whole.

Indicative content AO2 (applying understanding):

■ The range and scale of landforms associated with each process.
■ The timescale of the contribution, with changes in sea level over geological time but vegetation colonisation a short-term process.
■ The knock-on effect of changes in sea level, for example bar formation, which creates the coastal lagoon leading to deltaic infill and reed colonisation and also the fossil cliff line.

Question 3 (Eduqas AS style)

Evaluate the extent to which human actions have had a negative impact on coastal processes and landforms.   (15 marks, AO1 7, AO2 8)

(e) You will need to develop your ability to construct a sustained argument that is coherent, relevant, logically structured and substantiated with well-chosen examples.

Student answer

All human activities can be damaging to coasts and the greater the density of population and economic activity, the more this potential can happen. The key to the degree of damage is undoubtedly management as many coastal activities can conflict with each other. I am going to restrict my essay to human activities and not include any management of coastal erosion and flooding.

The coast is an important area for resources. There are lots of examples where resources have been badly developed and I am going to illustrate this with a couple of case studies.

My first is all about dredging for sand and gravel — they need this for building and also it has to be cleared away from harbour entrances so the ships can get in. The dredging disturbs the sea bed, so ruining the homes of fish and churning up the algae. This can affect food webs and so birds such as puffins which eat sand eels are in trouble. Also the spawning grounds of fish, e.g. Dogger Bank, are ruined so causing a decline in fish supplies.

Churning up sea beds can also release poisons from heavy metals and sometimes you get eutrophication. Along the south Devon coast the removal of offshore sands led to massive onshore erosion and destroyed several villages.

Another example which shows how bad human activities can be is getting oil out of the sea such as the North Sea, as oil rigs can explode or pipelines rupture, or tankers can have collisions, all of which can lead to disastrous oil spills, e.g. the Exxon Valdez which polluted the whole of the Alaska coast. The supertankers contain so much oil that if they hit the rocks the disasters are huge scale. Onshore the installations are ugly and give off fumes. However, the oil industry creates a lot of jobs and a lot of wealth too both locally and nationally.

My third case study is tourism, which is occurring on coasts all over the world. It creates a lot of resorts which bring in money and jobs (multiplier effect) but resorts create a lot of damage too like litter, pollution etc., e.g. at Blackpool. An interesting point is that sewage is a real problem, and it pollutes all the mussels.

So you can see from my three case studies how damaging human activities can be. It can be argued that they can be managed to avoid the damage, e.g. sustainable tourism, and also that these human activities bring in economic benefits such as employment and wealth.

I think that human activities are good for the coast provided they are managed and also that they do not occur in attractive areas in the coast where the scenery is beautiful or the ecosystems such as coral reefs have to be saved from extinction, e.g. GB reef in Oz.

e 6/15 marks awarded The answer does begin to get to the point of the question but is badly written, with a simple, basic style and a poor standard of English expression. The idea of three case studies could give a viable answer, but it needs amplification and better use of English. While there is some knowledge and understanding shown and there is a low level attempt to appraise the negative balance, overall it is a below-average answer.

A good idea, although it needs to be better expressed, is to define the limits of the focus, in this case *not* including management in human activities.

A possible mark for AO1 is Band 2 and borderline Band 1/2 for AO2. If the answer had been written in good English with precision of expression, and with more development, it had the potential to reach around 11/15 marks.

Indicative content AO1 encompasses knowledge and understanding of human actions and how they impact on both coastal processes *and* landforms. You could get credit for depth of exemplification or breadth of negative actions.

Note: human actions could include coastal management, which gives you much more scope.

Human activities include the following.

- Port activities — impact on land prices, destruction of ecosystems, threats of pollution.
- Land reclamation — impact on coastal processes.
- Tourism developments — impact on ecosystems such as coral reefs.
- Use of resources, such as minerals (oil, gas and sediments), biological resources (fish), space (sand dunes and tidal flats).
- Mineral extraction — sand and gravel dredging, impact on ecosystems, hydrocarbons — oil spills.
- Hard engineering approaches to coastal management.

AO2 requires you to demonstrate application of knowledge and understanding through an evaluation of the extent to which human activities have negative impacts. Relevant responses could include the following.

- The extent to which coastal management does have negative impacts — hard versus soft engineering, development of holistic, sustainable solutions.
- Resource extraction — if managed badly, e.g. fishing, oil, gravel extraction, can have negative impacts, especially on ecosystems.
- Land-based uses such as tourism — again an issue of management — or port development.

High-scoring answers will evaluate the capacity of human actions to be damaging, looking at scale, pace, sustainability etc.

■ Tectonic hazards

Question 1 (Eduqas AS style)

(a) The map in Figure 43 shows the first-arrival travel times of waves in the Boxing Day 2004 tsunami, following their generation at the earthquake epicentre. The numbers represent hours after the initial event.

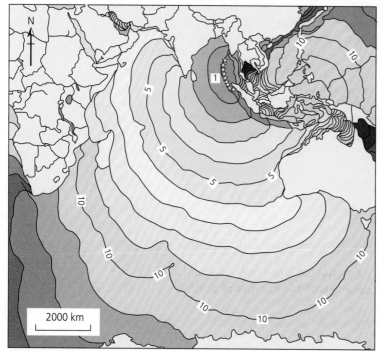

Figure 43 The progress of Boxing Day 2004 tsunami across the Indian Ocean
Source: NOAA

(i) Study Figure 43. Describe the temporal impact of this event across the Indian Ocean.

(6 marks AO3)

ℯ This question follows the format of Eduqas AS questions. This is a skills-based question so it relies on your accurate interpretation of Figure 43.

Student answer

(a) (i) The zone of fault rupture (epicentre) was from the Sumatra earthquake at the Sunda trench giving no warning to Aceh in Indonesia ✓. After 2 hours the wave had spread to Sri Lanka and southern Sumatra and Thailand ✓. Progress was much more rapid across the open waters of the Indian Ocean than to Java and northern Sumatra ✓. After 5 hours impacts had spread to the west coast of India and northwest Australia ✓. By 7–8 hours the waves had reached to the Somali coast and the southern Australia coast ✓. It is noteworthy that places such as Borneo and Brunei, much nearer, were reached at the same time as Antarctica ✓. The last places to feel the impact, some 24 hours later, included the Gulf of Thailand and northeast Australia — so there is not a clear correlation to distance ✓. Coastal configuration is clearly important as well as the degree of open water for the wave to move across✓.

ⓔ The marks are awarded in three bands based on the detail of description and the thoroughness of resource use.

Band 3: 5–6 marks

Band 2: 3–4 marks

Band 1: 1–2 marks

This answer achieves the maximum 6 marks for accurate analysis of the resource.

(a) (ii) Look at Table 22. Suggest and justify a statistical technique you could use to correlate the arrival time of the tsunami with the number of deaths. (4 marks)

Table 22 Human impacts of the Boxing Day tsunami

	Indonesia	Burma (Myanmar)	India	Maldives	Sri Lanka	Thailand
Deaths	169,000	81	10,750	81	31,000	5,300 (including 2,248 foreign nationals)
Missing	150,000+	1	5,550	n/a	4,000	2,800
Homes damaged or destroyed	200,100	5,000	15,000	15,000	100,000	60,000+
People displaced (some in relief camps)	600,000	10,000–15,000	140,000	11,500	500,000	300,000 (Burmese migrants a real problem)
Total population	217,500,000	48,956,000	1,041,410,000	309,000	19,287,000	64,340,000

Source: Geo Factsheet Number 194, www.curriculum-press.co.uk

ⓔ Try out the technique to see whether it works.

Student answer

(a) (ii) An ideal correlation technique is Spearman's rank (r_s) ✓.

$$r_s = [1 - \frac{6\Sigma D^2}{N^3} - N]$$

However, it would be necessary to obtain more information of deaths, perhaps adding four more sites such as Somali, Kenya, Andaman Islands, Malaysia etc., as ten items are needed for reliability and the table shows only six ✓.

Data by country, for example, India and Indonesia, also would need modifying as the tsunami hit various coasts at different times. The table needs to be used once the correlation has been calculated ✓ to ascertain whether the critical value has been exceeded and at what confidence level ✓.

ⓔ This answer scores the maximum 4 marks because the choice of technique is well justified.

(b) Study Table 22.

(i) Calculate which country had the highest percentage of deaths out of the total number of deaths (estimated at 275,000). (2 marks, AO3)

ⓔ For a calculation always show your working, because although you may get the wrong answer through a simple error, you will get marks for the method.

(b) (i) Answer is Indonesia

$$\frac{169,000}{275,000} \times 100 = 61\% ✓$$

(b) (ii) Suggest possible reasons for this. (4 marks)

(b) (ii) The earthquake was MM 9 ✓and the arrival of a very high tsunami was instantaneous with no chance to prepare for its onset in places such as Aceh as it occurred in shallow water offshore. Aceh was a poor, war torn province of Indonesia — with such huge damage of housing etc., this was bound to result in huge numbers of deaths ✓. It was possible that there was poor governance and little education and community preparedness in Indonesia, so the tsunami had maximum impact ✓.

ⓔ The maximum 4 marks are awarded for the correct calculation and good reasoning shown. There are many more alternative answers that you could develop based on your understanding of factors influencing disaster impact.

(b) (iii) Select and justify cartographical techniques you might use to show information on deaths and housing damage. (4 marks)

(b) (iii) Cartographical techniques could include proportional located symbols (circles, squares, bars of selected statistics superimposed on a base map) ✓; pie or bar graphs of selected statistics superimposed on a base map. These could be drawn to show a proportion of the total ✓. Both of these would best be shown using located data ✓. Choropleth maps could be used but are not especially suitable ✓.

ⓔ Answers that score well will select and justify through evaluation. The data must be easily read and interpreted and be able to be compared from country to country. For maximum marks, both deaths and homes destroyed should be covered and techniques will be well selected and justified. This answer shows some ideas but they are too generalised and not linked well to the data, so 2 marks only are awarded.

(c) Using Figure 43, Table 22 and your own knowledge, analyse the appropriateness of possible long- and short-term responses to manage and mitigate the impacts of tsunamis. (12 marks, AO1 5 and AO2 7)

ⓔ This is a wide-ranging question. One way to structure your answer is to use a framework such as the Hazard Management Cycle or Park's response curve to include the temporal scale of short-term and long-term management. The question also includes 'mitigate' and 'manage' so clearly you have to consider both.

AO1 content encompasses knowledge and understanding of short-term responses which occur immediately after the tsunami in the rescue period and during the first weeks of recovery, whereas long-term responses occur as a result of planning and development in the rehabilitation period, normally up to 20 years after the event.

Mitigation may include some protection and monitoring strategies which are part of the overall management process.

For AO2 you need to demonstrate the application of knowledge and understanding through an analysis of the appropriateness of the responses, e.g. did they work and was money well spent so that mitigation and management would improve in future disasters. You should give context as required, for example, Chile, Boxing Day (Asia), Solomon Islands or Tohoku (Japan).

High-scoring responses will consider:

■ whether the efforts were well managed by governments, charities and other agencies
■ whether the short-term funds were efficiently disposed of
■ whether the funds were spent on appropriate priorities in a well developed sequence, long term
■ whether the most vulnerable people were given priority
■ how well all the players worked together
■ whether accessible and remote areas were equally well managed
■ for the longer term, whether a legal framework for land tenure was established and whether local people were empowered to develop resilience and key features.

Note there are many aspects that could be covered, especially in the context of Park's disaster-response curve, or the Hazard Management Model (before, during and after the hazard event).

(c) To assess the appropriateness of the response to tsunamis I will look at the Boxing Day tsunami, which was one of the greatest mega disasters of all time, affecting 18 countries of varying levels of development and also because of their location at varied distances from the tsunami centre (see Figure 43) with Aceh in Indonesia the worst hit area as it was beside the epicentre.

Pre-disaster there were a number of factors that influenced the severity of the impact including level of development, standard of governance, population density, degree of sophistication of infrastructure (e.g. the high value Thai resorts filled with foreign tourists) as well the physical nature of the area — lowland coastal plains are particularly vulnerable to tsunami flooding, especially if unprotected by mangroves and coral reefs. Pre-existing strategies for community preparedness and education also increased the potential for mitigation as in Bangladesh.

At the point of disaster impact, physical factors played a huge role in influencing the number of deaths and the degree of damage, with clear distance decay away from the epicentre. The low level of the coral atolls of the Maldives meant they were actually overtopped by tsunami waves, causing much damage. Clearly, further away from the epicentre, the more potential for communication networks to deliver warning. Even so, although in Kenya evacuation plans were carried out, in neighbouring LDC Somali Republic with very poor governance there were significant deaths even though the tsunami waves travelled 5000 km across the ocean, as no warnings were given. So the result of this was that both pre-disaster and impact-wise it was not a level playing field.

e This is a long introduction — is it sufficiently focused?

(c) Short term an Oxfam report recorded that the massive emergency relief effort was tremendously successful in virtually all areas, as there were minimal secondary deaths from starvation or disease epidemics for lack of clean water. Even though temporary schools had to be constructed for 500,000 children by UNICEF, 97% of children returned to school within a month. So in spite of the large scale of deaths (275,000) and the complexity of identifying the 2500 tourists who died in Thailand, emergency relief did the business.

However, the geography of recovery varied considerably. The resilience of communities was dependent on death profiles, the extent of damage and the timelines and effectiveness of assistance. The cohesiveness of the community and the access it had to social, economic and political resources played a critical role in the community's recovery. The biggest single problem was the destruction of infrastructure and communications and meant the multiplicity of NGOs and government organisations lacked planes and boats to reach remote communities.

A year on in the rehabilitation phase again there was differential progress, often between neighbouring communities on the same coast. In Thailand, Phuket was rushed back on to its feet to revive the tourism trade in contrast to Krabi, which was totally ignored. The Cash for Work Programme was an appropriate scheme, designed to provide work for survivors by rebuilding boats, so they could return to fishing, or desalinating land, so they could return to farming, or craft-working opportunities to replace some of the million lost jobs across southeast Asia.

One big issue was that there was a shortfall between money pledged and money received and used and the speed it was released for use.

Another issue was the competition between charities and an over explosion of eye-catching projects such as logo sponsored fishing boats unsuitable for use.

Longer term progress in re-establishing infrastructure and public services and rebuilding housing has been very slow even after a decade of reconstruction (see Report Boxing Day Tsunami — a decade later). The greatest barrier to progress is problems associated with proving land ownership. In Sri Lanka in a desire to prevent a reoccurrence of the disaster, all houses, including fishermen's, have been built on land behind a buffer zone away from the coast to avoid risk and there have been numerous allegations of corruption. There have been huge arguments about building priorities as the authorities pushed for luxury hotels as opposed to rebuilding homes for local people.

There has been differential spending not only between but within countries.

One appropriate long-term project was the building of the Indian Ocean Tsunami Warning System which should provide warning to avoid tsunami disasters by establishing evacuation routes.

In conclusion, there are questions in many of the countries about the appropriateness of many of the longer term efforts at mitigation and management of tsunamis.

ⓔ 6/7 out of 12 marks awarded This student has shown good knowledge of some of the short-term, and a few of the long-term responses, but the early part of the answer is of peripheral relevance and the long-term responses are not always brought up to date, so the answer lacks balance.

Band 2 description for AO1 is appropriate, but for AO2 more information is needed. It is a moderate answer.

Indicative content:

Short-term responses include:
- search and rescue for survivors
- assessment of damage and destruction to homes
- provision of food and shelter and emergency accommodation
- first aid and medical provision to address injuries and disease onset
- clearing of infrastructure to allow access, e.g. ports, airports, roads
- water and emergency aid from national governments and international agencies such as the Red Cross and NGOs.

Long-term responses include:
- rebuilding of housing and other infrastructure such as schools and hospitals to move people away from temporary camps
- provision of employment opportunities, for instance, new boats for fishermen
- provision of training and education and community preparedness schemes, e.g. tsunami recognition and escape routes

- building of warning systems (Indian Ocean)
- rebuilding and remodelling of coastlines, new natural defences, land use changes in high risk areas, relocating buildings away from coast.

(d) Either:

(i) Explain why **both** earthquakes and volcanoes produce tsunamis as secondary hazards.   (14 marks)

Or

(ii) Explain how physical hazard **profiles** can be used to compare tectonic hazard events.   (14 marks)

e To help you answer these questions two essay plans have been produced. A sound and logical structure is essential in essay questions, so careful planning is vital.

(i) Explain why *both* earthquakes and volcanoes (key words, KW) produce tsunamis as secondary hazards (key definitions, KD)	(ii) Explain how physical hazard *profiles* (KD) can be used to compare tectonic hazard events
■ Define secondary hazard ■ Define tsunami as a wave generated by rapid movement of sea bed as a result of tectonic activity ■ Earthquakes involving vertical displacement at a subduction zone cause tsunamis ■ Especially powerful if earthquake focus is shallow and near land ■ Volcanoes cause tsunamis more rarely (5%) after catastrophic eruptions, e.g. Krakatoa 1883 VEI 6 caldera collapse leading to tsunami wave ■ Volcanoes could also generate tsunamigenic landslide	■ Define hazard profile ■ It measures physical characteristics such as magnitude, speed of onset, duration, areal extent, spatial predictability, frequency ■ The comparison can be within categories of earthquakes so earthquake profiles can be compared either with similar magnitudes or just overall profiles to look at social and economic impacts ■ Also the three types of tectonic hazards can be compared to explain, for example, why earthquakes are such killers compared with volcanoes

For (i), exemplar support plus precise explanation will lead to a Band 3 answer.
For (ii), exemplar support plus precise details of profiles is vital.

e It is the explanation of tectonic processes using technical terms and the relevant exemplification which leads to top band answers.

Question 2 (Eduqas style)

To what extent is the quality of governance the most important factor in the recovery of countries and communities from tectonic disasters?

(10 marks AO1, 5 marks AO2)

e AO1 content encompasses knowledge and understanding as to the importance of good governance as a factor in the recovery both nationally (countries) and locally (communities). Knowledge and understanding constitutes two-thirds of the total marks.

Questions & Answers

For AO2 you must demonstrate application of your knowledge and understanding through an evaluation of the extent to which governance is the most important factor, at both scales in the *recovery* phase from a tectonic disaster.

Student answer

I am going to explain the importance of governance as a means of managing a major tectonic disaster by looking at two tectonic events (Haiti and Christchurch 2010).

First I am going to look at Haiti as an example of bad governance (or I could do Nepal Gorkha earthquake 2015 or even Kashmir).

On January 2010 an earthquake (MM 7.0 so not a huge earthquake) struck the island of Haiti (the poorest LDC in the West). Its epicentre and focus was 25 km west of the capital Port au Prince which had around 2 million people. Clearly something went wrong as over 225,000 people were killed and 60% of buildings were completely destroyed making around 20% of Haiti's total people (around 1.8 million) homeless so there were about 2 million earthquake refugees who had to be housed in around 1300 squatter camps.

The initial response was dreadful as the port was destroyed and the airport closed because of the damage so they couldn't get emergency supplies in. The government failed to prioritise relief flights and there was a huge delay delivering emergency aid, some had to come in via the Dominica Republic which is at the other end of the island it shares with Haiti.

The real problem was that Haiti was such a poor country, as long-term social problems (no jobs) made the problems much worse. Haiti had had years of complete dictatorship (e.g. Papa and Baby Doc) and since 2006 a weak democracy which did nothing. The UN were already in Haiti trying to overcome the poverty (80% of Haitians were below the poverty line of $2 a day) and the earthquake scored a direct hit on their Haiti HQ and killed a lot of their employees. So there really was nobody in charge in the immediate emergency and the international aid and help was slow to get there (as explained earlier). In all fairness to Haiti, the earthquake was concentrated in the capital where 75% consists of urban slums. These urban slums were inadequately built and all the buildings collapsed so rescue efforts just couldn't get inside them and pre-earthquake 60% of the people didn't have access to toilets or piped water so there was bound to be a problem with disease — so it was all a desperate situation as shown on television programmes. They had to remove 19 million tonnes of rubble before they could start rebuilding.

Also during the recovery period there were further hazards (multi-hazard hot spot) such as cyclones and flooding and landslides from the deforestation of slopes. Then there was the cholera outbreak two years on which killed another 10,000 people in the camps, supposedly brought in by the Nepalese who were part of the UN recovery help force.

Haiti seven years later is limping in its recovery in spite of one or two good local schemes. There are huge disputes as to land ownership (no records or all destroyed in the earthquake).

Whether they will 'build back better' (UN Sendai framework 2015) is doubtful as the government is so bad. Maybe some of the NGO schemes in selected streets of the capital will work.

In my second example, Christchurch, New Zealand Darfield earthquake 2010 (7.1 MM) and Christchurch CBD aftershock 2011 (6.3 MM) does show the benefit of good governance. There were no deaths in the first one at Darfield and only 181 in the second in two large buildings and a bus! It was the second earthquake epicentre 5 km from Christchurch CBD which caused all the problems with 50% of the buildings redlined for demolition largely because of the huge amount of ground shaking (shallow earthquake) and liquefaction.

The emergency rescue operations were amazingly good with a good disaster rescue system and well organised and well-coordinated emergency management, although the mobile phone systems suffered meltdown as everyone rang up to see if their loved ones were safe.

Longer term, there were huge problems with 70,000 residents leaving the city, largely to suburbs and 50,000 people leaving their jobs (leading to raised unemployment except in demolition and rebuilding). Christchurch shopping centre and tourist trade was hit very hard with the temporary closure of many stores and hotels and the loss of port facilities for cruise ships at Lyttleton. Also buildings like the beautiful cathedral were destroyed. However, recovery and re-planning is going on at a great pace with renewal of 100+ km of water mains, 400 km of sewers and 1000 km of roads, also the traffic light system of buildings, red for demolition, amber for repair and retrofitting and green for repair grants has worked very well.

Huge progress is being made, with the revival of the shopping centre using old shipping containers and the rebuilding of facilities such as hotels and the new cardboard cathedral. And long term there is a major scheme to rebuild back Christchurch better which is working really well with plans for a redesigned CBD. Also the various Earthquake Commissions have been created to settle insurance claims and CERA to provide new homes for those who lost them have made remarkable progress.

So here good government provides a model example of a recovery that works as NZ is a well developed country, even if the damage figures were around NZ$130 billion.

So this tale of two earthquakes shows how important good governance can be, even if there are other factors. And it was not all perfect in Christchurch pre-earthquake as some authorities had flouted building regulations and also the geological survey had not made good maps as to where the fault and therefore areas of high earthquake risk were.

ⓔ 6/7 out of 15 marks awarded The strategy of comparing two earthquakes is really rather basic. A good plan with why governance is so important, giving multiple examples, would produce a more analytical response. Nonetheless the examples are factually sound and it is possible to award some AO1 credit. The big issue is the very descriptive style of 'whatever comes next' and the poor standard of English expression. There is mention of other factors, but the answer has to remain in the bottom band as there is limited explanation of these other factors and no real reference to countries and communities. In these long questions, sustained and detailed argument is very important.

A possible mark would be AO1 — low Band 2 (4/5 marks), and AO2 — Band 1 (1/2 marks).

Remember that you need both knowledge and understanding, and an evaluation of the question across the full range of tectonic hazards. For example, earthquakes are much less predictable than either volcanoes or tsunamis, or it is much easier to develop scales for magnitude of earthquakes (Richter, MM and Mercalli) than it is for volcanoes (VEI) or tsunamis.

AO1

- Good governance can occur at a variety of scales from the local (community council etc.) to regional, national (whether democratic or autocratic) and to international (role of UN and NGOs such as International Red Cross/Red Crescent or Oxfam).
- Good governance is vital in managing the hazard before the event (drills, evacuation routes, monitoring), during the disaster (emergency action) and in the recovery and rehabilitation in the post-disaster phase. It can direct, manage and coordinate in a non-corrupt way and recognise the need for outside help.
- The need for governance can be related to the nature of the disaster in terms of location and scale. The longer and more serious the disaster the greater the need for good governance. Localised disasters are more easily managed.
- Other factors could include the physical profile of the disaster, clearly magnitude is very important, and human factors such as the location of the disaster (accessibility, population density), the level of development as well as the type of governance.
- Useful examples for 'bad' governance could include Nepal and Haiti, or for 'good' governance, possibly Chile, China (Sichuan) or Japan (Tohoku).

For AO2, relevant responses might include the following.

- The relative importance of the other factors such as the physical profile of the hazard (magnitude, speed of onset, duration) and other geographical factors such as location, population density and, above all, level of development which may be related to quality and style of governance.
- The extent to which quality of governance varies in importance in different tectonic events.
- The extent to which government quality can change over time, or vary across a large country such as India or Indonesia.
- The application of quality governance as an issue in well selected examples.

Question 3 (WJEC style)

This question corresponds to section A of Unit 4.

Assess the importance of plate tectonics in understanding the distribution of earthquakes.
(6 marks AO1, 13 marks AO2, 1 mark AO3)

ⓔ These long questions require you to demonstrate your ability to develop a sustained line of reasoning that is coherent, relevant and logically structured — so quality of English is *very* important.

Student answer

The USGS estimates that several million earthquakes occur each year with the vast majority of minor significance. There is an inverse relationship between frequency and magnitude with approximately 15 earthquakes a year of MM 7+ and around 130 of MM 6–6.9.

The movement of tectonic plates causes pressure to build up in the Earth's crust. When the pressure is released a series of tremors known as earthquakes occur.

Consequently the global distribution of earthquakes is related to the location of plate boundaries, with around 85% of all earthquakes being related to plate movements at their margins (inter-plate earthquakes). The intense shaking motion, i.e. an earthquake, only lasts for a few seconds. The plane of rupture is called a fault and the location of the movement is the hypocentre or the focus.

The depth of focus which determines the amount of surface damage can be classified as follows:

Shallow focus: 0–70 km, intermediate focus: 70–300 km and deep focus: 300–700 km. Shallow focus earthquakes account for over 70% of all earthquakes.

At constructive (divergent) plate boundaries, magma pushes up the crust to form ridge and rift features, i.e. mid-ocean ridge, allowing gravitational force to slide the lithosphere away by a process known as ridge push. Transform faults along the ridges cause offsetting which leads to frequent minor earthquakes. This can also occur along the continental divergent boundary along the East African Rift Valley, for example, the recent Tanzanian earthquake MM 5.4, 2016.

So called collision boundaries such as those along the Alpine-Himalayan mountain belt also experience frequent, shallow earthquakes, largely because of thrust faulting in the compressed rocks so resulting in interior mountain ranges experiencing earthquakes (Nepal Gorkha 2015).

The most frequent earthquakes are experienced along all types of destructive boundaries as a result of the subduction of oceanic plates by the process of slab pull, a key driver of plate movement. These earthquakes occur in a narrow zone called the Benioff zone with foci ranging from shallow to deep as the oceanic plates are subducted underneath the continental plates. In western South America the Nazca plate is subducted beneath the South American plate, leading to the frequent occurrence of powerful earthquakes in countries such as Ecuador (2016), Peru (2011) and Chile.

The last type of plate boundary — conservative — leads to high magnitude earthquakes as two plates move laterally with each other, jostling past each other, as with the San Andreas Valley in California. The 'big one', which can be partially explained by gap theory, can occur when the plates get 'stuck' and large-scale pressures are released. Haiti 2010 was formed as a result of localised movement at a conservative boundary. Thus it can be seen that there are a variety of earthquakes (inter-plate) all caused by movements at plate boundaries, with a distinctive spatial geography — some 85% of all earthquakes.

However, there are many causes of intra-plate earthquakes not caused by plate marginal activity.

In Hawaii and the Galapagos, hot spot activity occurs as plumes move upwards leading to huge shield volcanoes. Some earthquake activity in islands such as Hawaii can be associated with volcanic activity.

Equally, in many areas of the world not on plate boundaries, earthquakes can be relatively common, although normally they are of low magnitude. Parts of interior USA such as New Madrid, Missouri, have experienced a number of earthquakes, likely to be associated with movement along old fault lines. Equally, in the UK there are numerous earth tremors and earthquakes around MM 3–4 where movement occurs along former faults, such as the Church Stretton fault which caused earthquakes in Shropshire.

A growing number of earthquakes are associated with human activities. The nuclear explosions such as the recent ones in North Korea have led to significant earth tremors. Moreover, the building of huge dams, such as the Three Gorges Dam in China, hold back huge weights of water in the very large reservoirs. Some scientists argue the increase in the number of earthquakes in Sichuan is linked to this. The Killari earthquake in India is another intra-plate earthquake linked to dam building. A recent controversy is the fracking for gas and oil which certainly causes many low magnitude earthquakes such as in eastern USA. The concern is raised as a frequent argument against developing fracking activity such as in Lancashire.

In conclusion therefore, plate boundaries are of fundamental importance in explaining the distribution of earthquakes, especially high magnitude ones, but there is a wide variety of causes — around 15% of earthquakes result from other causes.

🅔 **19/20 marks awarded, AO1 6 marks, AO2 12 marks, 1 mark AO3** This is a well informed and exemplified answer with good up-to-date knowledge of plate tectonics, which deserves Band 3 marks for AO1. The candidate also attempted to analyse the distribution and link to plate movements with a thorough and coherent analysis, so scoring well in AO2. The answer was also well written with sustained, detailed argument, so the 1 mark for AO3 is awarded.

Indicative content:

AO1 encompasses knowledge and understanding of the distribution of earthquakes.

- The crust of the Earth is mobile, so there is a slow build-up of stress with rocks and when the pressure is suddenly released, parts of the surface experience intense shaking, i.e. an earthquake.
- The global distribution of earthquakes is closely related to plate boundaries, i.e. inter-plate earthquakes.
- At constructive plate boundaries (divergence) shallow focus earthquakes occur at transform faults which cause offsetting at the mid-oceanic ridges — Mid-Atlantic and Mid-Indian Ocean ridges and also along the continental divergence zone of the East African Rift Valley.
- Shallow focus earthquakes can also occur at collisional plate boundaries on the Alpine–Himalayan belt where orogenies are taking place.
- Strong earthquakes can occur at conservative plate margins where two plates move laterally and jostle past each other — in California on the San Andreas fault.
- Earthquakes can occur at destructive (convergent) plate boundaries and their force varies from shallow to deep along the Benioff zone as slab pull drags one plate beneath another (the oceanic crust is subducted beneath the continental crust — Andean belt).
- They occur at hotspots such as Hawaii associated with volcanic activity caused by a rising plume.
- They also occur along old fault lines, such as those in Madrid in southern USA or those minor earthquakes in the UK (20–30 times a year) strong enough to be felt.
- Earthquakes can be induced by human activity, for example, the weight placed on the Earth's surface by the building of huge reservoirs — a possible cause of the Killari earthquake in India.
- Low magnitude earthquakes are also associated with the process of fracking for oil and gas, for example, in eastern USA, and are a major concern in all proposed areas such as Lancashire, UK.
- Earthquakes can result from nuclear bomb explosions, as in North Korea.

For AO2 you need to demonstrate application of knowledge and understanding through an overall analysis of the distribution of types of earthquakes (magnitude on MM scale and depth).

- Analysis could involve an attempt to quantify the number of inter-plate to intra-plate earthquakes — 85:15%.
- You could also look at earthquakes from natural causes versus growing numbers caused by human activity.
- Your analysis could also be related to depth of earthquake which in turn affects the magnitude and impact of an earthquake.
- You will need to provide details of distribution of various examples.
- Analysis should show good understanding as to how plate tectonics actually causes earthquakes using modern theory (slab pull etc.).

Knowledge check answers

Knowledge check answers

1 Beach nourishment or 'feeding' involves humans adding pebbles and sand to a beach to replace those lost to longshore and offshore movement, so balancing the budget deficit.

2 While the cells are discrete functional systems, there is movement across littoral divides, especially of fine material, so they are 'open'.

3 Equilibrium is upset by changes in energy conditions, for example, during a storm (physical factor), or by rising sediment impact from human actions, both of which can lead to rapid changes over short periods of time.

4 Threshold is the critical water velocity at which a particular size of load will be entrained or deposited. Fine material is very cohesive and therefore requires a higher threshold of current velocity than coarser sand.

5 These events are single occurrence events happening over a short period of time.

6 Wavelength (λ) is the horizontal distance between two crests or troughs. Wave amplitude is the height of the crest above stationary water — not the same as wave height which is the vertical distance between a crest and a trough. Wave frequency is the number of crest and troughs passing a stationary point over a time period, such as a minute.

7 It cuts down the rate of erosion and therefore cliff recession rates as the waves do not break but are reflected back from the cliff, usually in deep water.

8 A rotational landslide is a downslope movement of material that occurs along a distinctive curved slip surface. A slump is the result of the rotational slide, when a portion of the steep slope moves forward for only a short distance.

9 The platforms are formed by erosion and salt weathering during tidal exposure as well as by wave quarrying and abrasion so the more general term is more accurate.

10 Sorting by waves and tides operates via the Hjulström curve whereby the deposits are entrained and deposited according to the velocity and size of the pebbles. An example is storm beaches whereby only large boulders are hurled up the beach beyond high tide level.

11 This is a direct result of the size of the sand grains which can easily be bounced along.

12 Physical factors: sediment supply can enhance or diminish the available silt; changes in river currents and volume can affect erosion; storms can erode the marsh; change in tidal currents can increase erosion and alter species; changes in wave direction, nature and size can affect marsh stability: climate affects species types, growth rates and sea levels; sea level rises can upset equilibrium and destroy the marshes. Human factors: commercial, industrial and recreational activities can damage the marsh.

13 A cocktail is a mixture, and in this case this 1 in 200 year event resulted in extreme physical factors (storm surge 1.3 m, extremely high spring tides and very strong 130 km h⁻¹ onshore winds) combined with unfavourable human factors (poor quality coastal defences [railway owned] and also widespread building of holiday bungalows and mobiles on the flat coastal plain).

14 Eustatic change is when the sea level changes worldwide because of the volume of water in the oceans, for example, because of climate change. Isostatic sea level changes result from an increase or decrease in the height of the land, as a result of ice ages or sediment deposition or tectonic activity and occur locally.

15 A ria is a submerged, non-glaciated valley and a fjord is a submerged glaciated valley.

16 High latitude coasts have extremely cold climates with limited economic potential and are often seasonally ice-bound.

17 Statistical techniques, through a process called frequency analysis, are used to estimate the probability of the recurrence of a given precipitation or flooding event using data analysis. So this event has a 1% chance of occurrence in any given year.

18 Where high value and high risk installations such as nuclear power stations are under threat from rapid erosion.

19 Managed realignment avoids hard engineering solutions and retains the natural ways of estuary zones. It also provides conservation potential as the new habitats will develop into high quality, ecofriendly environments. Avoidance of coastal squeeze. Cheaper option so there are opportunities to offset costs with income from tourism. Benefits should be evaluated against potential problems.

20 Avoid areas of high value marine ecosystems and fish spawning grounds and areas landward of the 20 m isobaths. Prevent industrial-scale dredge mining.

21 Pioneer vegetation leaves much bare ground which is subject to wind erosion.

22 Consult expert opinion and avoid conflicts. Collect and analyse data about coastal processes, existing defences, land use and built environment, and the natural environment. Set out objectives. Consider the options: do nothing, hold existing line of defence, build out to protect shoreline, retreat to a new line inland. Publish a plan and review it.

23 It is difficult to reconcile the conflicts between environmental, economic and social sustainability and the views of multiple stakeholders who place increasing pressures on the coast and also contrasting locations along the coast with different needs.

24 The mantle.

25 African, Eurasian, South American, North American, Pacific, Indo-Australian, Antarctic.

26 a The most violent earthquakes are found at destructive plate boundaries and transform boundaries.

b The most explosive volcanoes are found at destructive plate boundaries or are supervolcanoes associated with continental hotspots.

27 A fault scarp is the initial slope formed by faulting which is eroded to form a fault line scarp over time.

28 A fold mountain building period.

29 The earthquakes are linked to the disposal of drilling waste water deep underground in disposal wells, not the actual act of drilling. The earthquake occurs when the deep well disposal of waste water intersects with naturally occurring fault lines.

30 The difference is one of location. When molten rock is still located within the Earth it is known as magma. When molten rock reaches the surface and is extruded, it is known as lava.

31 A smaller earthquake or tremor that follows a major earthquake. In Christchurch, the second earthquake was thought to be an aftershock. Like many other aftershocks it was significant because it occurred in the city centre, so causing huge damage.

32 The theory predicts the relative size and frequency of earthquakes in a given area.

33 Using Tohuku as an example, the primary hazard was the earthquake, the secondary hazard was the tsunami and the tertiary hazard was the nuclear power station disaster caused by the flooding from the tsunami.

34 An active volcano is a volcano that has had at least one eruption during the past 10,000 years. A dormant volcano is one that is not erupting nor is expected to, but could erupt again in the future as it has in historic times. An extinct volcano has not had an eruption for at least 10,000 years and is not expected to erupt again in a comparable timescale in the future.

35 The volcano had not erupted since 1845 and the eruption was very small-scale initially. The disaster was caused by lahars, for which a hazard risk map was prepared but was not available. Lahars also hit and rapidly engulfed a large town, Armero, in the middle of the night.

36 The difference lies in location. The focus is the exact point inside the crust of the Earth where the quake begins. The epicentre is the point on the Earth's surface directly above the focus.

37 The earthquake killed many students in schools because of timing and poor building quality. For many families their only child was killed.

38 Certain conditions are required in combination: fault and uplift in coastal zone or nearby ocean, high magnitude (MM 6+ earthquake), vertical displacement, shallow focus of earthquake.

39 Almost all events could be chosen, but look for issues of building design, building development in hazard-prone areas or over-confidence that they will be immune from disaster, e.g. Mt Merapi, where people live in a volcanic-prone area.

40 Increased building and higher densities of population in high risk cities, areas often in shanty towns; deforestation increasing landslide risks after earthquakes; removal of protective vegetation (mangroves and corals) which protect coastlines from tsunamis.

41 An area in which many hazards (climatic and tectonic) occur within a concentrated area. The one type may exacerbate the other type, e.g. hurricanes and lahars in the Philippines.

42 Possible precursors include any changes from the norm, e.g. small-scale, frequent earthquakes, bulging on the side of the volcano, changes in gas emissions, ground deformation, changes in water temperature of streams.

43 Resilience is toughness, coping capacity and recovery time. Recovery is the stages in getting over a disaster, both immediate short term and long term. Rehabilitation is the ability of communities to overcome the psychological upset of a disaster.

Index

Index